Farm Policies and Our Food:
The Need for Change

A report by the National Consumer Council

Published by the National Consumer Council

20 Grosvenor Gardens London SW1W 0DH

Telephone/Minicom 0171 730 3469 Fax 0171 730 0191

March 1998 PD 11/B2/98

ISBN 1 899581 36 7

Price £14

About the National Consumer Council

The National Consumer Council is the independent voice of consumers in the United Kingdom.

It is our job to represent the interests of the consumers of goods and services of all kinds, whether publicly or privately supplied. We ensure that those who take decisions affecting consumers - and particularly policy-makers in government, parliament, industry, business and the professions - have a balanced and authoritative view of their users' interests before them. And we make sure those views are taken into account.

We take a keen interest in essential household services like water, gas and electricity where competition, and therefore consumer choice, is often limited. And we have a special brief to represent the interests of consumers who are least able to make their voices heard.

Quality and value for money in the goods and services consumers use or buy every day are central to our work. When we are investigating the provision of any product or service, we focus on seven key consumer tests - access, choice, safety, information, equity, redress and representation.

The Council was set up by the government in 1975 and is largely funded by the Department of Trade and Industry.

A wholly-owned subsidiary of the National Consumer Council, **NCC Services Ltd**, offers consultancy advice to public-sector and utility organisations wishing to improve their services to consumers.

For more information about the National Consumer Council

Please send for the latest issue of the *NCC Bulletin* with up-to-date news about our publications, policies and campaigns.

We can usually arrange for you to have our publications in braille, on audio-tape, on computer disk (in WordPerfect) or in large print - please contact us for details.

National Consumer Council
20 Grosvenor Gardens
London SW1W ODH

Telephone/Minicom
0171 730 3469
Fax 0171 730 0191

Contents

Acknowledgements

This report is based on research by European Research into Consumer

Affairs (ERICA) and was prepared for publication by Jill Johnstone,

Head of Policy at the National Consumer Council.

We would like to thank all those who read and commented on the text.

ERICA can be contacted at:

Arbour House

The Mount

Fetcham

Leatherhead

Surrey KT22 9EB

Tel 01372 372905

Fax 01372 376487

1. Executive summary

Consumers, particularly those on low incomes, want and need access to cheap food, but not at the expense of safety. Policy-makers must find a delicate balance between the need for mass-produced cheap food and their responsibility to ensure production methods do not endanger public health and safety, and the environment.

Several issues will affect the development of food production over the next decade – negotiations in the World Trade Organisation (WTO) and Codex Alimentarius Commission (Codex) on agricultural trade and food standards, and talks on the expansion of the European Union (EU) eastwards. It is crucial that the impact of farm policies on consumers informs these talks.

We have argued for many years that the Common Agricultural Policy (CAP) acts against consumers' interests and is in dire need of reform. This argument is supported by the considerable amount of research we have undertaken and published on this issue. As we said of the CAP in 1988: 'It overcharges consumers for food; it reduces consumer choice, it has an adverse effect on food quality; it disregards nutritional advice; and it harms consumers indirectly by contributing to environmental damage and the disruption of international trade' (1). While some reforms have been introduced in the 1990s our criticisms of the policy are as valid now as they were in 1988.

Our report examines the impact on consumers of national and European policies governing farm production processes in terms of the price, choice, safety and quality of food. It does not examine environmental and animal welfare impacts, not because we do not believe that these are important, but because other organisations are doing this. Nor does the report examine safety issues arising further down the food chain as this would require another volume.

Chapter 2: The Common Agricultural Policy

In this chapter we outline the background of the CAP and its impact and cost implications for consumers and taxpayers, and the overall impact on the EU economy. We also look at choice and quality of food, and intensive farming.

Chapter 3: Animal feed and the BSE crisis

The BSE crisis is a clear example of the dangers of a policy which sidelines consumers' interests in favour of a supply-led approach to food production. The intensive farming encouraged by the CAP almost certainly gave rise to BSE. This chapter examines the spread of BSE and how the UK government and the Commission failed to act soon enough, or to appreciate fully the public health implications.

Chapter 4: Hormones

Consumers have been concerned about the implications of hormones in milk and meat production for some time. This chapter covers the different hormones and their uses in agriculture. It concludes that despite issues of public health the need to contain surpluses, caused by the CAP, was the driving force in introducing bans on hormone use.

Chapter 5: Antibiotics

In this chapter we look at the effects of antibiotic residues in food and the growing bacterial resistance to antibiotics used to treat humans. This is a particularly serious problem as consumers food choice cannot protect them against the risk. The high prices guaranteed by the CAP have encouraged farmers to intensify and as a result to use more antibiotics.

Chapter 6: Pesticides

The risk to human health from pesticide contamination is still significant. Chapter 6 considers the effects of residues on and inside food and the health issues associated with this. It also looks at the contamination of drinking water and the huge clean-up costs which consumers have to bear. Regulation was slow to appear and is inadequately monitored. And re-evaluating older pesticides has only recently been introduced in the EU.

Chapter 7: Fertilisers and the nitrate problem

The CAP's high support prices have encouraged the increased used of fertilisers. In this chapter we examine the problems of nitrate residues in food and water and the shortcomings of the Nitrate Directive.

Chapter 8: The application of biotechnology

Development of regulation has not kept pace with the technological advances in this field. The novelty of biotechnology is in itself a problem – as yet no adequate risk analysis exists. Using two examples chapter 8 considers the emergence of genetically modified products and the potential risks, and benefits, to consumers.

Chapter 9: A new direction for agricultural policy

In this chapter we look at the shortcomings of the European Commission's recent proposals for CAP reform – Agenda 2000 – and suggest a way forward. Using examples from Sweden we show how effective better farming methods can be.

Chapter 10: Reform of regulation

The EU has developed rigorous testing procedures for agricultural inputs which form part of its regulations to protect the health and safety of consumers. In chapter 10 we consider the effectiveness of this regulation, and its monitoring and enforcement. We argue that the EU should promote the 'precautionary principle' – used where there is a potential serious threat to human health and the environment, even if certain cause and effect relationships are not established scientifically.

Chapter 11: The international framework

This chapter outlines the international framework in which UK and EU policy operates, considers its likely impact on consumers, and makes proposals for reform. It focuses on the Codex Alimentarius Commission (Codex), the World Trade Organisation (WTO), and the 1994 Uruguay Round Agreement.

Summary of recommendations

The Council of Ministers should:

- change incentive systems by establishing a more market-oriented policy which brings prices more into line with consumer demand. Phase out quantity restrictions and export refunds, and reduce import levies. It should also phase out compensation payments and replace them with 'fully decoupled' direct payments;

- fund advisory programmes which encourage farmers to adopt production methods that enhance the quality of their produce and reduce the use of antibiotics, pesticides and nitrates. Such programmes should also form part of agricultural training courses;

- fund research and development of less intensive farming methods with a focus on improving both agricultural efficiency and the quality of output;

- extend the EU ban on the use of mammalian meat- and bone-meal to all animal feed, and thoroughly evaluate the production processes using the precautionary principle;

- introduce a compulsory full ingredient labelling scheme for all animal feed;

- keep the current ban on the use of hormones in meat, and the moratorium on the use of BST in milk production in the EU in place;

- prohibit the use of antibiotics as growth promoters throughout the EU. Antibiotics should only be used when an infection is diagnosed and under veterinary direction;

- make sufficient resources available to DG XXIV (Consumer Policy) to enable it to monitor compliance with EU regulations in member states; and

● amend the Product Liability Directive to make the inclusion of primary agricultural products in national legislation compulsory.

The European Commission should:

● ensure that the programme for the systematic re-evaluation of old pesticides is quickly and strictly implemented;

● develop a system for ensuring that maximum residue levels (MRLs) are not exceeded for pesticides and nitrates in food and drinking water;

● bring forward proposals: for improved identification and registration of sheep and pigs along the lines of that for cattle; for compulsory treatment records for farm animals to enforce the hormone ban and tighter regulations on the use of antibiotics;

● ensure that monitoring of agricultural produce takes place in each member state to ensure compliance with EU regulations; and

● co-ordinate and make publicly available the findings of surveillance on residues of veterinary medicines, pesticides and nitrates in foodstuffs.

The international community should:

● include a consumer impact analysis in the forthcoming reviews of the WTO standards agreements and, if the agreements are found to operate in a way which discourages improvements in standards and consumer information, agree to reform them; and

- agree to reform Codex by:

    adopting a full freedom of information policy;

    committing additional resources for better representation of consumer and developing country interests;

    opening up the expert committees to consumer participation; and

    reducing the dominance of food producers and requiring all experts who receive funding from industry to declare the details in a public register.

2. The Common Agricultural Policy

Established by the Treaty of Rome of 1957 which created the European Community, the Common Agricultural Policy (CAP) is often seen as the cornerstone of the European Union (EU), particularly up until 1992 and the creation of the Single European Market, when it was the major common policy binding the member states together. Its aims, set out in Article 39 of the Treaty, are:

- to increase agricultural productivity by promoting technical progress and ensuring the rational development of agricultural production and the optimum utilisation of the factors of production, in particular labour;

- thus to ensure a fair standard of living for the agricultural community, in particular by increasing the individual earnings of persons engaged in agriculture;

- to stabilise markets;

- to assure the availability of supplies; and

- to ensure that supplies reach consumers at reasonable prices.

Essentially, the CAP is an agricultural support policy, the core element of which is a system of market price support. In simple terms, and allowing for variations from product to product, the CAP guarantees minimum prices to farmers for their produce. Each year the farm ministers of the 15 member states meet to agree the guaranteed minimum prices, generally known as the support prices. It attempts to maintain these prices by intervening in the market place and either buying up excess produce and putting it into storage or by subsidising exports to non-EU countries. It also operates a series of import quotas which restrict the amounts of goods that can come into member states from non-EU countries as well as levying tariffs on those imports to ensure that they do not undercut EU product prices.

More recently there have been attempts to reform the CAP, notably through the 1992 MacSharry Reforms. There have also been pressures to reform the CAP from the international community through the General Agreement on Tariff and Trade (GATT), now the World Trade Organisation (WTO). The MacSharry reforms, in tandem with agreements made in the Uruguay Round negotiations of the GATT, completed in 1994, have led to reductions in market support prices for agricultural produce in the EU. Instead of simply supporting market prices, agricultural support under the reformed CAP has to some limited extent 'decoupled' (separated) the support of farm incomes from agricultural production by giving direct payments to farmers under a variety of compensation schemes. This is particularly the case in the cereals sector where support prices have been significantly reduced.

In July 1997 the European Commission published further proposals for CAP reform in its report *Agenda 2000* which considers the action needed to prepare the EU for enlargement to take in central and east European countries. These proposals continue the shift away from price support towards direct income support started with the MacSharry reforms (see chapter 9).

We, and other consumer organisations, have been very critical of the CAP which places considerable burdens on consumers both in terms of the cost, choice and quality of food.

The costs to consumers and taxpayers

First, the CAP places a heavy burden on taxpayers. It is a major drain on the EU budget accounting for the lion's share of overall spending. Throughout the 1970s and 1980s it rarely accounted for less than 60 per cent, at times rising to 75 per cent or more. In 1988 a ceiling on CAP price policy spending was introduced but it still accounts for 50 per cent of the budget.

In 1996 the cost of the CAP to EU taxpayers was 56.2 billion ECU (£46 billion). However, this is an underestimate as the CAP induces additional expenditure from national budgets to implement some of its structural schemes. Many member states also provide additional assistance to agriculture. The Organisation for Economic Co-operation and Development (OECD) calculates that the member states spent an extra 12.3 billion ECU (£10.1 billion) in 1996 (2).

The use of guaranteed prices, intervention buying and import duties as the main CAP support mechanisms has had the direct effect of increasing EU food prices. This hidden food tax places a particular burden on low income consumers who spend a higher than average proportion of their income on food. Little or no official EU information is published on this aspect of the CAP. However other organisations have estimated the consumer cost including the OECD (see table 1). These show that consumers pay a heavy price for the CAP, however, the burden of support is shifting towards taxpayers. In 1996 the proportion of the policy's cost falling on consumers fell below 50 per cent. However, this was partly the result of the unusually high world cereal prices and the 1995 figures probably provide a more accurate picture. Nevertheless the MacSharry reforms have had a positive impact in reducing the burden on low-income consumers and increasing the policy's transparency.

10

Table 1 The cost of the CAP to consumers and taxpayers in billion ECU

	Consumer cost [1]	Consumer cost as % of total	Taxpayer cost	Taxpayer cost as % of total	Total cost to consumers and taxpayers
1986-88	69	67	34	33	103
1990-92	69	62	43	38	112
1993	64	58	47	42	111
1994	63	59	45	41	108
1995	58	54	48	46	106
1996	39	41	56	59	95

[1] measured as the difference between world and EU prices.

Source: OECD, *Agricultural Policies in OECD Countries: Measurement of support and background information 1997*, Paris, June 1997.

However, there is no room for complacency. Further reforms are required. The food price effect varies considerably from product to product. Table 2 summarises OECD calculations for the main groups. It shows that for cereals, pigmeat and eggs consumer costs are now very small. In 1996 the figures were positive meaning that the subsidy was in favour of consumers as world prices rose above internal market prices. However, for some products, notably rice, sugar, milk and beef a significant part of the price paid to producers is still a subsidy paid by consumers. The Commission's Agenda 2000 proposals (see chapter 9) include reforms to the beef and dairy sectors but there are none to the sugar and rice regimes.

Table 2 Consumer subsidies as a percentage of producer prices 1979 to 1995

	1979-81	1986-88	1990-92	1993	1994	1995	1996
Wheat	-24	-50	-43	-35	-28	-11	10
Maize	-32	-47	-45	-36	-29	-28	-4
Other grains	-29	-55	-49	-49	-50	-30	-1
Rice	-8	-58	-51	-57	-52	-56	-43
Sugar	-30	-69	-58	-59	-46	-41	-48
Milk	-40	-54	-56	-51	-50	-49	-44
Beef and veal	-37	-47	-48	-53	-56	-55	-53
Pigmeat	-14	-28	-21	-25	-23	-12	2
Poultry	-21	-33	-31	-29	-30	-29	-19
Sheepmeat	-47	-64	-57	-27	-35	-36	-23
Eggs	-13	-19	-15	-9	0	-11	7
All products	-28	-44	-41	-39	-38	-34	-29

[1] a minus sign indicates a tax on consumers

Sources: OECD, *Agricultural Policies in OECD Countries: Measurement of support and background information 1997*, Paris, June 1997.

The overall impact on the EU economy

While estimates vary, all the studies show that the consumer and taxpayer costs of agricultural policy are much greater than the benefits. OECD figures for 1996 suggest that the total cost of the CAP and the national policies of the member states to consumers and taxpayers was 95 billion ECU, while the total benefit to farmers was 67 billion ECU (3). In other words, every 100 ECU that farmers gain costs consumers and taxpayers about l42 ECU. While this is a significant improvement on earlier years – the ratio has in the past reached 100:180 – it clearly does not represent value for money.

It can also be criticised on grounds of fairness. As most support is production-related it follows that the bulk of it goes to larger farms. An analysis of EU farm incomes during the 1980s concluded that large farms 'had far higher incomes' per person employed than the smaller or medium-sized units. In addition while the incomes of small and medium farms remained steady or declined slightly during the 1980s, those of the larger farms had increased – particularly in the later part of the decade. In 1988 the average income per person on the smallest farms in the EU was less than 10 per cent of that on the largest. It is a thoroughly regressive policy – the costs fall disproportionately on low-income consumers and the benefits go disproportionately to better off farmers. It has contributed to the growing gap between rich and poor in the EU (4).

Over the years the CAP has led to a massive misallocation of resources in the EU. First, much of the effect of high support prices is absorbed in higher factor prices, particularly land and, more recently, in quota values. This raises the capital investment, obstructs structural adjustment and makes it very difficult for new farmers to enter the industry. Thus the ability of the industry to develop and become internationally competitive is severely constrained. Second, resources have been diverted into agriculture which could have been put to much more beneficial use. The CAP has not created jobs. Employment in agriculture has fallen sharply throughout the EU – from an average of 12 per cent of the working population in 1968 to less than 6 per cent in 1992. In the EU overall around 6 million people are mainly employed in agriculture. However, nearly 40 per cent have another source of earnings and only about 2.2 million farmers are classified as full-time. The only solution to the problems this loss of jobs poses for the rural economy is to develop alternative employment opportunities outside agriculture (5).

Choice and quality

While the price and availability of sufficient food may be consumers' primary concern, matters such as food quality, the range of foods available, environmental considerations and animal welfare are becoming increasingly important.

The final choice about what to eat should be one for consumers themselves (backed by accurate and informative labelling). Consumers can only make choices from what is available in the shops. At present, the CAP operates in a number of ways which affect the kinds of products which are available.

Measures designed to deal with the milk surplus, for example, have subsidised the sales of butter and other full-fat dairy products to schools, the armed forces and elderly people. Reduced-price sales of butter to biscuit, cake and ice-cream manufacturers encourage its use instead of healthier alternatives.

Market management mechanisms in the fruit and vegetable sector fail to take account of consumers' interests. They operate not only to keep prices in the shops high, so discouraging the consumption of foods which nutritionists advise consumers to eat more of, but also to limit the range and quality of the produce reaching the market. The tailoring of the grading system to keep prices up at times of surplus, rather than to meet consumer needs, has resulted in perfectly sound but small fruit being banned from sale. Yet many consumers, particularly those on low incomes or with small children, might choose to buy this fruit in preference to larger, more expensive pieces.

Reforms to the fruit and vegetable regime were agreed in 1996. These shift the emphasis away from support prices. They are a welcome step forward but it remains to be seen what impact they will have on prices and consumer choice.

Intensive farming

The CAP has encouraged the use of intensive farming methods. Although, as in other industries, modernisation and rationalisation over the last fifty years has been inevitable, CAP support mechanisms have distorted the economics of food production. High support prices have encouraged farmers to concentrate on quantity regardless of market demand. They have led to inflated land prices providing further incentives to maximise output per hectare. This has resulted in greater use of chemicals such as antibiotics, hormones, pesticides and fertilisers. Consumer concerns about these developments range from:

- the effects on food safety and long-term health;

- the effects on nutritional quality of food;

- reductions in flavour and texture of many foods, particularly meats;

- the implications for animal welfare; and

- the impact on the environment.

Conclusion

The CAP is an expensive policy. It absorbs half the EU budget and imposes a substantial burden on consumers through higher food prices. It is also inefficient and inequitable. The costs to consumers and taxpayers greatly exceed the benefits to farmers. The cost burden falls disproportionably on low-income consumers and the benefits go disproportionately to higher-income farmers. It has not created the jobs the rural economy so badly needs. However, its adverse impact is not purely economic, it also affects food choice and quality. It has encouraged farming methods which are damaging the environment, have an adverse impact on animal welfare, and raise serious concerns about food safety and long-term health.

3. Animal feed and the BSE crisis

Bovine Spongiform Encephalopathy (BSE) is a fatal, degenerative brain disease affecting cattle. It was first recognised in the UK in 1986 since when 162,047 cases have been confirmed affecting 35,000 farms, with a peak of 34,370 cases in 1993 (6). The total number of cases in other countries is approximately 400, half of these are in Switzerland and the rest in other member states or in non-European Union (EU) countries which had imported animals or animal feed from the UK (7).

It is believed that BSE is caused by a natural protein, called a prion, which when folded up in the wrong way causes other similar proteins to change into the same shape (8). Although the origin and transmission route of the disease have not yet been fully elucidated, the source of the UK epidemic seems to lie in animals given feed which included the remains of animals containing the abnormal form of the prion. The practice of feeding cows animal remains is a consequence of attempts to maximise output and lower costs as part of the process of intensification of agricultural production since the second world war. Offal and the remains of dead animals were rendered down and incorporated into animal feed.

The UK epidemic seems to have been caused by the recycling of infected cattle and sheep tissue as cattle feed and by a change in the rendering methods – involving lowering the temperature of the industrial process. In the late 1970s and early 1980s, the market for tallow declined. As a result the processes of hot solvent extraction and solvent recovery (used to extract the tallow) were omitted in the period 1981 to 1982. Both the change in the process and the relatively high fat content remaining are thought to have allowed infective agents to survive (9). Once the cattle themselves had the disease, their remains too became a source of infection. Until 1996 there was no evidence that the

Regulation: animal feed

Common regulation began in 1970 with the creation of the first Standing Committee for Feedingstuffs. In 1979, a Council Directive (79/373/EEC) was adopted on the marketing of compound feedingstuffs. Users of feedingstuffs must be provided with accurate and meaningful information regarding the analytical constituents and ingredients present in compound feedingstuffs. These ingredients should be included in product labelling. However, there is no obligation for producers of animal feed to provide full labelling. Since 1991, it has been compulsory to declare contents whether as specific ingredients or by category, for example, cereal grains, legume seeds, milk products, land animal products, fish products. Bloodmeal could thus be listed as such or as land animal products. It is not considered practical to draw up a positive list for ingredients in animal feed as some suitable plant might accidentally be excluded and new developments ruled out. Instead a negative list is set out in regulation 15 of the UK feedingstuffs regulations 91/516. This excludes, for example, any material which contains faeces or urine, household waste, treated hide, wood or sawdust, sewage and restaurant waste, except that discarded for reasons of freshness. It was updated in 1995. Regulation 96/25 lists suitable feed materials, but for guidance only, not as an exclusive list. The Standing Committee on Animal Feedingstuffs is considering new measures to oblige feed manufacturers to declare the ingredients of animal feed. In the UK the feed industry has agreed to do this on a voluntary basis and over 90 per cent of feed has full ingredient listing.

In 1995, a Council Directive (95/454/EC) was adopted to fix the principles governing the organisation of official inspections in the field of animal nutrition. Since the BSE crisis, EU checks at national level are being reinforced. New rules on inspection and enforcement apply from 1 April 1998.

disease could be transmitted from one animal to another. However, a recent study by the UK's Central Veterinary Laboratory seems to indicate that vertical transmission, that is from cow to calf, can take place (10).

In June 1988 legislation was introduced into the UK making BSE a notifiable disease, with the destruction of suspect and confirmed cases. The European Commission later added BSE to the list of EU notifiable diseases (11). In July 1988 the feeding of meat and bone-based meal derived from ruminants to cattle and sheep was prohibited in the UK. The Commission introduced a ban on the feeding of mammalian proteins to ruminants in all member states in 1994 (12).

BSE and Creutzfeldt-Jakob Disease (CJD)

BSE belongs to a group of diseases called 'Transmissible Spongiform Encephalopathies' affecting both humans and animals. The group includes scrapie in goats and sheep and CJD in humans. CJD is a rare but incurable and fatal neurological disease. It was first identified in the 1920s and is a worldwide phenomenon with an incidence order of one case per million per year. There are two forms of the disease: classical CJD and a new variant, recently identified, known as nv-CJD.

Classical CJD can be divided into three forms: a sporadic form (about 85 per cent of cases); forms associated with genetic predisposition (10 per cent of cases) and infection resulting from the transmission of infected human tissue, for example from corneal grafts or the practice during the early 1980s of using growth hormone obtained from human cadavers to treat growth deficiencies. The sporadic and genetic forms of CJD almost always affect elderly people (mean age of onset about 65) with patients dying four to six months after the onset of the disease. The incidence of classical CJD at a rate of about one case per million per year has remained at a stable level in the UK and does not seem to vary whether a country has BSE or not (13).

In 1989 the report of the working party on BSE, known as the Southwood Report, stated that the risk of BSE to people was 'remote' but said that 'if our assessments of these likelihoods are incorrect, the implications would be extremely serious'. In announcing the report, the UK government stated that 'independent experts have concluded that BSE is most unlikely to have any implications for human health' (14). Until March 1996 the UK government maintained the line that there was no link between CJD and BSE.

In 1989, however, a ban was announced on Specified Bovine Offal (SBO) (including the brain, spinal cord, spleen, thymus, tonsils and intestines of cows over six months old which had died or been slaughtered in the UK) in all foods for humans. This action aimed to remove from the human food chain the raw material most likely to present a danger of transmitting BSE (15).

Between March 1995 and January 1996 the CJD surveillance unit in the UK identified eleven cases of a new form of CJD (16). These patients were all young (between the ages of 19 and 41, with an average age of 29) and had had the disease on average for 13 months. The scientists studying these cases have found nothing in the patient's medical history, genetic analyses or other factors which could explain them (17). The UK Secretary of State for Health announced the findings of the Spongiform Encephalopathy Advisory Committee (SEAC) which had examined these cases on 20 March 1996. They concluded that 'although there is no direct evidence of a link, on current data and in the absence of any credible alternative the most likely explanation at present is that these cases are linked to exposure to BSE before the introduction of the SBO ban in 1989' (18).

Similarly, while stressing that no link between BSE and nv-CJD had been proven, the WHO meeting of experts in April 1996 concluded that the most plausible hypothesis for the appearance of nv-CJD was the UK population being exposed to BSE.

Two recent studies, one by SEAC and the other by the Institute for Animal Health in Edinburgh, confirmed the BSE link to nv-CJD (19). In December 1997 MAFF announced a ban on sales of beef on the bone. This announcement followed evidence from SEAC that the agent responsible for BSE had been found in dorsil root ganglia and bone marrow (20).

Reaction within the EU

The response to the March 1996 announcement was an immediate fall in consumption of prime and processed beef. In the UK it was reported to be 55 per cent and 45 per cent respectively of the previous year's consumption figures by April 1996 (21). Similarly, beef consumption fell in other European countries: France 30 per cent, Belgium 15 per cent, Portugal 50 per cent and Italy 60 per cent (22). Most EU member states introduced national bans on UK beef imports. In March 1996 following consultation with the Standing Veterinary Committee (SVC), the Commission introduced a temporary worldwide ban on exports of UK live cattle, semen, embryos, meat and meat products from cattle slaughtered in the UK and intended for human and animal consumption. It also included medicinal, cosmetic or pharmaceutical products and mammalian meat- and bone-meal (23).

Overall beef consumption in the EU had dropped by 7 per cent by the start of 1997 (24). The Commission expects that it will recover by 2001. The UK government, however, has expressed the opinion that this is an over-optimistic estimate (25). Importantly, while beef sales may have recovered from the slump of 1996 the consumption of beef products has noticeably declined. Burger sales, for example, are down 40 per cent on 1995 levels (26).

The UK government programme for the eradication of BSE

In March 1996, as a result of public concern about the safety of UK meat, the UK government decided to take a number of additional measures to those taken in 1989:

- the destruction of animals over 30 months – known as the 'over thirty months scheme' (OTMS) – and their exclusion from the human and animal food chains;

- a ban on the feeding of mammalian meat- and bone-meal to all farm animals;

- the removal of specified bovine material from carcasses and its controlled destruction; and

- reinforced controls in slaughterhouses, rendering plants, feed mills and farms.

In order to move towards a lifting of the temporary ban on exports of UK beef and beef products, the UK government also submitted a framework document detailing its programme for the eradication of BSE in the UK. The Commission required that the framework document be approved by the SVC and, more importantly, given what the Commission termed, 'considerable misgivings about the effectiveness of past actions taken by the UK in relation to BSE', that Community inspections should take place to verify the correct and effective implementation of the following steps:

- implementation of a selective slaughter programme of that part of the UK herd at risk of developing BSE through exposure to contaminated feedstuffs;

- introduction of an effective animal identification and movement recording system with official registration;

- legislation for the removal of meat- and bone-meal from feed mills and farms and subsequent cleansing of the premises and equipment concerned;

- effective implementation of the OTMS including the destruction of carcasses; and

- improved methods for removing specified bovine material from carcasses.

At the meeting of the Council of Ministers in Florence in June 1996 the UK framework for eradicating BSE in the UK was agreed. In order to secure a gradual lifting of the export ban the UK had to convince the Commission and the SVC that the required actions had been taken.

Consumer concerns

Too little, too late

Criticisms of both the Commission and the previous UK government on their handling of the BSE crisis have focused on what the Economic and Social Committee of the EU called 'their relaxed, if not negligent, attitude to the possible gravity of the public health implications of their approach' (27). Reimer Boge, the chairman of the European Parliament's independent committee of enquiry into BSE, which reported its findings in January 1997, accused both the Commission and the UK government of trying to 'minimise the problem' (28). It has been suggested that public health protection took second place to the major economic interests at stake with experts' views ignored for economic and political reasons. The absence of proof of risk was interpreted as proof that there was no risk (29). In its criticisms of the UK government, the Association of Metropolitan Authorities argues that, 'the government simply hasn't been prepared to listen to concerns raised by food safety experts outside the confines of [its] own research programmes' (30).

There has been a great deal of criticism of the poor enforcement and control measures taken by the UK Government and EU institutions which led to a failure in the implementation of legislation drawn up to eradicate BSE and to minimise the risks to public health. These failings apply to a number of areas including animal feedstuffs, the detection and traceability of animals, and slaughter house procedures and inspection. There has also been criticism of the inadequacy of labelling, preventing consumers making informed choices. For the purposes of this report we consider policy on animal feedstuffs and detection and traceability.

Animal feedstuffs

The European Parliament enquiry has suggested that inadequate enforcement and control measures in the UK meant that the UK ban on feeding meat- and bone-meal to cattle, first applied in July 1988, only fully came into force in July 1996. In 1994 a general ban on the feeding of mammalian proteins to ruminants was introduced in all member states (31). Some 26,000 cows found to have BSE were born after the feed ban was announced so it is clear that this ban was not fully observed (32). In addition, the latest scientific evidence suggests that vertical transmission was taking place. MAFF, for example, believes that new stocks of feedstuffs may have become contaminated with old stocks during storage on the farm (33). Similarly, it is not clear that feed manufacturers in the UK rigorously applied the ban in all mills resulting in cross-contamination from machinery previously used to make feed which included animal remains (34).

In addition, through a loophole in the UK regulations, UK feed manufacturers exported more than 70,000 tonnes of potentially infectious animal feed containing meat- and bone-meal after the domestic ban was introduced on the sales of such products in 1988 (35). This was exported to France, Israel and Thailand. Israel is one of the few non-EU countries which has reported a case of BSE (36).

The UK's chief veterinary officer, Keith Meldrum, admitted to the European parliamentary enquiry that, with the benefit of hindsight, the UK could have applied controls on contaminated feed more effectively but that the UK had taken corrective steps in March 1996. In 1995 the Commission required the UK to introduce a formal monitoring programme of feed mills (37). The programme of sampling began in February 1996, eight years after the original ban came into force.

In June 1996, MAFF announced a scheme to recall, from manufacturers and farms, residual stocks of feed that might contain meat- and bone-meal. This was followed by a ban making it illegal to hold such feed from August 1996. In addition, the UK has introduced a ban on the use of any ruminant material in all animal feed including that for pigs and poultry. Feed manufacturers in the UK have agreed on a voluntary basis to declare the content of animal feeds although they are not currently obliged to do so.

In addition to the criticisms of the UK and EU authorities response to the BSE outbreak, the SVC has been criticised for failing to set adequate standards in the production of meat- and bone-meal in the first place. The German feed expert, Professor Oscar Riedinger of Stuttgart University, told the parliamentary enquiry that the SVC had gone against all microbiological practice in agreeing, in 1990, that in the manufacture of animal feeds meat- and bone-meal need only be heated to 133 degrees for twenty minutes. He asserted that experts on the committee knew that feed made from mammalian meat- and bone-meal should have been heated to 140 degrees. The directive was subsequently amended in 1994 (38).

Detection and Tracing

The checking scheme in place before August 1995 for the export of live calves relied on signed statements by sellers and exporters that calves intended for export were not progeny of BSE-infected dams (39). A sample of computer records was cross-checked by MAFF against these statements.

On 21 April 1997, EU agriculture ministers adopted a Council regulation on cattle identification and labelling of beef products (40). It required all EU countries to introduce computerised systems for tracing cattle by the end of 1999 and that all cattle born after 1 January 1998 must have an eartag in each ear and a passport. Farmers must also keep an up-to-date register of their cattle. An EU-wide compulsory beef labelling scheme will be in force from 1 January 2000 but member states can opt out of this for sales of beef in their own country.

Conclusion

The causes of the BSE outbreak are still not clearly understood. We hope that the public enquiry announced by the UK minister for agriculture in January 1998 will bring more information about the origins of BSE into the public domain. What is clear is that the public health implications were not given sufficient weight by the UK government of the day or the Commission. The supply-led approach to food production promoted by the CAP, encouraged both the intensive farming methods that almost certainly gave rise to the disease, and the regulatory authorities response to it, in which the economic interest of producers took precedence over public health.

4. Hormones

Hormones are substances naturally produced in the body which are essential for normal physical and mental growth. In food production, the term hormones is used generically to cover a wide range of substances administered to animals for therapeutic purposes, that is to treat illness, or for the purposes of promoting growth by speeding up the weight gaining process. Farmers use a number of different hormones in meat production:

- Anabolic hormones, which enhance the conversion of food into muscle and are divided into two types: first 'natural' (or endogenous) hormones, which are chemically reproduced copies of the hormones which occur naturally in animals, such as testosterone, progesterone, and oestradiol 17B. Second, synthetic (or xenobiotic) hormones, which do not occur naturally in animals but enhance the effects of natural hormones. Examples include trenbolone, zeranol and diethylstilboestrol (commonly known as DES) part of the stilbene family of hormones.

- Beta-agonists, which vets use therapeutically against asthma or to prevent miscarriages in animals, but farmers also use as growth promoters to encourage the production of muscle instead of fat. Clenbuterol is the most well-known example.

- Anti-hormones or thyrostatic hormones which inhibit the function of the thyroid gland and thereby have an influence on hormones that control body growth so that animals absorb more water and gain weight more quickly as a result.

- Corticosteroids which encourage water retention in muscles.

Generally speaking, by increasing the speed at which animals gain weight and by encouraging a greater ratio of muscle to fat, the use of growth-promoting hormones decreases the time it takes for cattle to be ready for slaughter and can produce a leaner type of meat. The use of certain hormones, for example, may produce an 8 to 25 per cent increase in the daily rate of weight gain and a 7 to 15 per cent gain in feed efficiency (41). As a result, farmers' profit margins can increase.

Consumer Concerns

Public concern over the use of hormones in farm animals came to the forefront in Europe during the 1970s. This was linked to news reports in Italy about babies developing breasts and enlarged genitals after eating canned baby food made from French veal containing traces of the synthetic hormone DES (42). It is suggested that exposure to strong doses of natural hormones can lead to the development of secondary sexual characteristics and may play a role in the appearance of certain cancers (43). The risks associated with synthetic hormones are seen to be greater because they accumulate more easily in organs such as the kidneys. DES, for example, was first introduced 35 years ago as a compound forming the basis of certain medicines in the treatment of pregnant women but scientific studies on women who used these drugs have shown that the substance may be carcinogenic and increases the risk of miscarriage.

In 1995 the European Commission's scientific conference on growth promotion in meat production backed earlier scientific studies which suggested that, at present, there is no evidence for possible health risks to the consumer due to the use of the 'natural' sexual hormones in growth promotion since the residue levels of natural hormones are extremely low. The daily production of sex hormones by humans is much higher than the amounts possibly consumed from meat even in the most sensitive humans. However, other experts have argued that any increase in the level of hormones above that which occurs naturally imposes a potential additional risk of carcinogenic effects. The vital caveat to all the safety clearances is that they are provisional on producers following good veterinary and agricultural practice. For example, producers should follow the advice on withdrawal periods for hormone treatment before the animals are sent for slaughter, and the hormones should be implanted in a part of the animal which will be discarded at the slaughterhouse, such as the ear.

The clinical consequences of continued exposure to residues of potentially highly active beta-agonists are still unclear and, as a result, their use as growth promoters is seen as inappropriate because of the potential hazard for humans and animals (44). Exposure to high residues of beta-agonists can be particularly dangerous. In 1990, for example, 135 people in Spain and 22 in France were hospitalised after eating liver contaminated with clenbuterol (45). It is also thought to have been a factor in the deaths of three farmers in Ireland who inhaled the drug when mixing it with feedstuffs (46).

It is still unclear what possible harmful effects the corticosteroids may have on humans (47). There is a suggestion that they may have a negative effect on the immune system of animals. As a result, they are also seen as inappropriate as growth promoters because of the potential hazard for human and animal health (48).

The uncertain effects on human health of combining various growth promoting substances also cause concern. The Commission's 1995 scientific conference on growth promotion in meat production emphasised the need for further study of the effects of growth promoters administered in combination, in which the presence of one may disturb the metabolism of others.

European Union regulatory response

Before the 1980s most rules concerning growth promoters were fixed on a national basis. However, prompted by the demands of consumer groups concerned about possible adverse effects on human health, and in an attempt to harmonise the rules in the various member states, the first substantive piece of Community legislation concerning hormones and meat production came in July 1981 (49). This prohibited certain substances that have a hormonal action and all substances that have a thyrostatic action. It included:

- an immediate ban on stilbenes (of which DES is one) and thyrostatic substances;

- a general ban on substances with oestrogenic, androgenic or gestagenic action (sometimes called sexual hormones) with the exception of certain specified uses, such as therapeutic purposes (which were allowed subject to restrictive conditions and controls); and

- allowing national rules to continue to apply in the case of five specific substances used at the time for fattening animals, namely oestradiol 17B, progesterone, testosterone, trenbolone and zeranol.

The Commission was required to submit a report before July 1984. Following scientific advice, which suggested that the proper and appropriate use of certain 'natural' hormones presented no risk to human and animal health, the Commission presented proposals in June 1984 which provided for the controlled use of the three natural hormones for fattening animals. However, the European Parliament and Council of Ministers rejected this approach and insisted on a total ban.

Subsequently, in December 1985 the Council adopted a directive confirming a ban on the use of all substances for fattening purposes and established detailed rules allowing restricted use of some of these substances for therapeutic or zootechnical purposes. This directive, however, was annulled by the European Court of Justice on procedural grounds but its terms were re-adopted by the Council in March 1988 prohibiting the use in livestock farming of certain substances which have a hormonal action (50). The UK voted against the ban although it was subsequently adopted.

Unfortunately for consumer groups, the majority of whom strongly support the ban, the European Union (EU) introduced the ban mainly for supply control reasons and did not wait for its scientific committee to report on safety. The agriculture commissioner at the time, Frans Andriessen, made it clear publicly that it was a political decision, motivated by concern about the EU beef surplus on the theory that the hormone ban would reduce both domestic beef production and beef imports and thereby reduce the size of the beef mountain. As a result, the hormones ban is contested by some countries, in particular by the US which itself allows the use of the 'natural' hormones, testosterone, progesterone, and oestradiol 17B for fattening animals, together with the 'synthetic' hormones zeranol and trenbolone. Canada, New Zealand and Australia also allow the use of such hormones. The case has been brought to the disputes settlement procedure of the World Trade Organisation (WTO) (see chapter 11).

Enforcement

Under a Council directive (51), and as part of the measures to guarantee observance of the ban, member states have to present annual residue control plans, which give full details of the substances they intend to search for, the number of samples planned, the analytical methods to be used and so on. In the UK this is undertaken by the National Surveillance Scheme (NSS) set up in

1980 which, as well as monitoring hormones, also monitors residues of antibiotics, nitrofurans, organochlorine and organophosphorus compounds. The Commission checks that these plans conform with the directives.

There is evidence that, although member states have become much more active in their campaigns, the illegal use of hormones is still a persistent problem within the EU (52). It is driven by the increased profitability, reckoned to be about 10 per cent, achieved by using hormones. In January 1995 a report, supported by the Commission and published by the Belgian consumer magazine *Test-Achats*, suggested a high presence of hormone residues in beef meat and beef livers in a random survey of food outlets in twelve member states. In Belgium, for example, 22 per cent of beef liver samples contained residues of the beta-agonist clenbuterol and in Spain that figure was around 35 per cent. Figures obtained in the UK seem to indicate that the problem is not as acute. Less than 2 per cent of beef contained residues of anabolic hormones and less than 4 per cent of beef livers contained clenbuterol. Similarly, the UK's NSS programme seems to indicate abuse is not widespread or frequent in the UK. In 1991, for example, 0.3 per cent of samples found excess levels of 'natural' hormones (53).

There is concern, however, that the monitored figures could represent the tip of the iceberg with illegal users adopting increasingly sophisticated techniques to avoid detection (54). In March 1996, in a speech to the European Parliament, Franz Fischler, the commissioner for agriculture, expressed his concern about the growing sophistication in the illegal production and use of 'cocktails' of substances. These are difficult to detect because of the low levels of individual substances which evade standardised screening techniques but which, when combined together, have powerful growth promoting effects (55). This may account for the reduction found in samples by surveillance teams (56). Similar considerations may explain why some producers apparently use injections, rather than implants, of steroid hormones, which could prevent their detection at slaughter and potentially allows the sale of meat containing very high concentrations of hormones (57).

Such trends have worrying implications for consumer health in that illicit users, who are avoiding detection, are unlikely to be following correct procedures for dosage and withdrawal periods and, therefore, hormone residues are more likely to exceed recommended maximum residue levels (MRLs) in food products.

Because of public concern, and under pressure from the European Parliament, the Commission decided in 1990 to undertake a comprehensive review of how the legislation on residues in fresh meat was being implemented. Following their (confidential) study, the Commission sent a communication to the Council and to the Parliament in April 1993 which drew attention to the widespread availability and apparent use of illegal growth promoting substances and to the deficiencies and difficulties of member states in taking effective counter-measures (58). In particular, the report confirmed serious weaknesses in several key areas including applying the hormone ban, detection of fraud, and in the quality of the testing. A lack of effective organisational arrangements and doubts about the real commitment to tackling the problems were seen as important demotivating factors for those seeking to implement the directives on the ground.

In addition, in September 1993 the Commission issued proposals for two new regulations to replace existing directives on growth promoters. These are designed to:

● clarify and codify the existing directives on prohibiting the use of hormones for fattening animals, and to add beta-agonists to the list of banned substances for all uses except the therapeutic treatment of horses and pet animals (the main intention was to prevent use of beta-agonists in calf-fattening units);

- clarify and improve control procedures for the detection of residues in live animals and in meat, ensure a more focused application of resources for testing, and reinforce sanctions; and

- amend the CAP beef regime as a preliminary step towards the adoption, under Commission powers, of more comprehensive measures against farmers using illegal substances, for example, by removing their eligibility for Community aids.

The European Parliament endorsed the Commission's approach. However, discussions in the Council have moved more slowly. At this stage, while there is broad consensus among the member states on the measures to improve controls, differences of view remain on the prohibition of use of beta-agonists and on the most appropriate review procedures for new and existing substances with a growth-promoting effect in animals.

In seeking to reinforce the effectiveness of the ban the Commission sponsored a major scientific conference on growth promotion in meat production in 1995. Its objective was to survey the scientific evidence and to help develop better strategies and measures by identifying the risks associated with particular practices and substances, and by providing the most up-to-date knowledge on ways of detecting illegal uses. To improve residue surveillance and control strategies, the conference concluded that:

- control authorities must be aware of possible changes in the patterns of use of growth promoting substances so as to better target sampling and testing strategies;

- in principle, the use of multi-residue procedures is the most effective approach for residue control programmes although more difficult and costly;

- attempts should be made to harmonise laboratory testing standards throughout the EU; and

- collaboration between testing laboratories and exchange of information on substances in use on the black market should be encouraged.

In addition, to improve effectiveness, surveillance should take place on farms and at slaughter plants and must involve targeted, as well as random, sampling. There should also be monitoring at the retail level to give an indication of the effectiveness of the farm and slaughter plant control system. Overall the sampling strategy should be more directed and covered by quality assurance to give a common high standard throughout the EU. A common standard and mode of implementation for residue control strategies throughout the EU is necessary to ensure that the data from individual countries' control activities allow for valid comparisons to be made (59).

It has been suggested that farmers should have to keep records of which cows are treated by veterinary medicines. At the moment, producers can avoid prosecution when an animal is tested positive, for example, for a beta-agonist, by claiming that a vet prescribed the drug for therapeutic treatment. It is difficult, therefore, to bring a case against users unless inspectors actually find the illegal substances on site. In Italy all farmers have to keep records, countersigned by a vet, of medicines used on each animal. These records must accompany each animal (60).

In the aftermath of the murder in February 1995 of a Belgian veterinary inspector who had been engaged in combatting the illegal use of growth promoters, the European Parliament passed a resolution denouncing the lack of action by the Council of Ministers and called on it to urgently adopt the Commission's proposals. In March 1996 the Council, despite UK objections, reached political agreement on the proposals. These include financial penalties on producers who are found to have used hormones illegally. They would lose beef premiums and compensatory aid payments for one year after the first offence and for five years if repeated. This was seen by the Council as taking a firm step to reassure consumers and to stamp out illegal use. In Ireland, for example, legislators have proposed the additional measure of publishing a list of processing plants that have handled cattle treated with illegal growth promoters. This is aimed at encouraging greater vigilance among meat processors (61). It remains to be seen whether these measures will lead to better enforcement.

Bovine Somatotropin (BST)

Bovine Somatotropin (BST) is a protein or peptide hormone produced by genetic engineering. Its function is to direct energy input from feeding to the mammary gland to the detriment of fat storage. Administered by injection, it can increase milk yields in cows by between 10 to 20 per cent (62).

BST has been surrounded by controversy since it became known that it was being tested in secret trials in the UK. This raised the level of public awareness of the use of medicinal products as production enhancers and added to the pressure for broader assessments of non-therapeutic drugs. However, since the hormone acts in a species specific way and is not active in humans, the European Medicines Agency's Committee for Veterinary Medicinal Products (CVMP) which advises the Commission on licensing, has accepted that the residues from BST do not, in principle, present any health risk for consumers of meat or milk obtained from animals treated with the product (63).

In spite of scientific opinion the Council of Ministers has consistently maintained a ban on the use of BST within the EU under a Council decision concerning the placing on the market and administration of BST. The ban was extended in 1991 and 1993 (64). A further extension in May 1996 keeps the ban in place until 31 December 1999 and authorises member states to carry out tests on the use of BST (65). Before July 1998 the Commission is to submit a report to the Council on the conclusions of the studies carried out so far so that more information is available when a definitive decision is taken. The Council decision does not impose barriers to dairy product imports into the Community from countries where BST is authorised.

The ban imposed by the Council reflects a number of concerns of European policy-makers. As the 1993 Commission report to the Council of Ministers on the implications of licensing BST suggested, uppermost in the Commission's mind were concerns about over-production of milk within the EU. As a result, the authorisation of BST with its implications for encouraging increased quantity rather than quality did not fall within the new guidelines for the CAP. Further, BST is linked to intensive production systems and needs careful and highly structured feed management which tends to encourage an undesirable change in farm structure towards larger and more intensive units (66). There is also a view that BST does not constitute a significant revolution in milk production methods since growth in milk production can be successfully obtained by other means, such as animal selection, without any major drawbacks for animal welfare or human health. Instead there is a fear that the use of BST will lead to a loss within the EU of breeds with greater genetic potential because of increased difficulty in distinguishing those naturally higher producing animals (67).

The Council is also concerned that using BST in milk production might prejudice its image as a natural product and lead to a drop in consumer confidence. The Commission, for example, supported a number of consumer surveys in Germany, France, Italy and the UK covering about 70 per cent of the EU population. These surveys found that the introduction of BST might trigger a reduction in consumption of milk by up to 20 per cent in the countries polled. With heightened consumer concern over food quality and safety affecting sales, this would have repercussions for producers right along the food chain (68).

Consumer groups see few advantages resulting from any increased production as a result of the use of BST. The EU price support system prevents them from benefitting, in terms of lower prices, from any significant increase in milk supply and indeed perhaps means they have to pay more, as taxpayers, to support the additional costs of increased dairy products going into intervention stores. Any fall in consumer confidence as a result of BST's authorisation may ultimately raise costs for consumers (69).

Consumer organisations have also argued that if the Commission authorised the product consumers should be able to choose whether they consume milk produced with BST. Milk production is currently pooled and not separately identified. This makes creating transparency and suitable labelling difficult. It is in the interests of competition that those producers who seek to gain any commercial benefits from using BST should also bear the market risks. Without labelling, farmers using BST will impose the commercial risks associated with it on to other dairy farmers and to the dairy industry as a whole.

There are concerns about animal health as a result of BST's use, particularly the increased occurrence of mastitis – an inflammation of the udder – in cows.

The increased use of antibiotics to treat mastitis as a result of BST use may have implications for residues in milk and, by implication, for human health (see chapter 5). There are fears that using BST could become a substitute for good herd management. In addition, research carried out by the Institute Nationale de la Recherche Agronomique seems to indicate that the use of BST could contain the risk of triggering a virus existing in a latent state in a healthy animal carrier. US studies suggest that cows treated with BST give birth to stillborn and deformed calves more often than untreated cows and, in a few cases, the same problem has been found in untreated daughters of *treated* cows (70). Some people have argued that the animal health costs outweigh the benefits of the extra milk products. The Codex Alimentarius has recently delayed a decision on the use of BST for another two years (71).

Conclusion

The European regulatory authorities have taken a precautionary approach to regulation on the use of hormones in both meat and milk production. However, while consumer concerns about health and safety may have played a part in decision making, the driving force in both the ban on the use of hormones in meat production and BST in milk was the need to contain the surpluses caused by the CAP. The extremely poor enforcement of the ban on the use of hormones in meat production in many member states demonstrates this.

5. Antibiotics

As a now frequently used medicinal product, it is perhaps easy to forget that the era of antibiotics actually began relatively recently. Perhaps the most well known antibiotic, penicillin, came into use in 1940, although the first antibiotics for the treatment of human bacterial diseases were introduced in 1935 (72). Their widespread use in food production began in the early 1940s. In animals, antibiotics are used in three ways:

- as therapeutic agents to treat bacterial diseases;

- prophylactically to prevent and reduce the incidence of these diseases; or,

- as growth promoters added in low concentrations to water or animal and poultry feed.

Appendix 1 describes the regulatory regime for veterinary medicines, including antibiotics.

Consumer Concerns

Consumer concerns regarding the use of antibiotics in food production focus on two main issues. First, the direct impact on human health from antibiotic residues in food and second, the *indirect* impact from the risk of bacterial resistance arising from their widespread and prevalent use as growth promoters.

Residues in food

Concerns about the possible toxic effects on humans of antibiotic residues in food focus mainly on therapeutic or prophylactic use, although there are some concerns over background residues creating hypersensitivity to antibiotics in humans (73).

In the 1980s when, for example, one in eight pig kidney samples had levels of sulphonamide in excess of the permissible maximum residue level (MRL), there was considerable concern about residues in farm animals. Since then levels of abuse have declined. In 1990 0.4 per cent of 46,000 tests undertaken by the UK National Surveillance Scheme to monitor residues showed traces of antibiotics above the MRL. There was a reduction from 15 to 5 per cent of excess MRLs between 1986 and 1990 largely accounted for by a more thorough tracing back procedure identifying farms supplying offending samples, plus improved campaigns to vets, farmers and the feed industry (74).

In spite of this there are still a number of areas of concern. There is some evidence that not all European Union (EU) countries have been stringent in implementing the surveillance procedures and in preventing improper use of antibiotics. In a written question to the European Commission in July 1996 Martina Gredler, MEP, produced evidence that in Germany residues of the antibiotic Chloramphenicol, banned in the EU in June 1994, was found in a high percentage (in some cases 20 per cent) of meat samples taken by the German authorities. Similarly, although therapeutic antibiotics are not normally authorised for use in egg-laying poultry flocks because of the risk of residues in eggs, the antibiotic lasalocid has been found in some egg-laying flocks (75). A European consumer survey showed mixed results (76). Traces of antibiotics were found in 17 per cent of samples of pork in the Republic of Ireland. In Spain traces were found in 7 per cent of veal samples and 5 per cent of pork samples. In the UK traces were found in 7 per cent of turkey samples and 4 per cent of pork samples.

Bacterial resistance to antibiotics used to treat humans

Since antibiotics were first introduced scientists have noticed that, with their outstanding capacity to adapt, bacteria have succeeded in becoming resistant to many of the compounds used to combat them (77). Over the last 40 years many bacteria have become resistant to several ordinary antibiotics. The concerns surrounding the use of antibiotics as additives in feedstuffs are related to the increasing numbers of antibiotic-resistant bacteria and the fear that humans and animals could become prone to incurable diseases. Small doses of antibiotics given against quite benign bacteria can contribute to selecting much more aggressive strains since only the strongest and most virulent in every generation survive (78). Animals that are continuously fed with antibiotics have been found to have a predominance of resistant intestinal bacteria (79). Further, a relationship seems to exist between the use of antibiotics in a country and the percentage of bacteria that appear to be resistant (80). A worrying phenomenon is the increasing number of bacteria that have become multi-resistant, that is, resistant to a number of antibiotics. One explanation of this multi-resistance is that different antibiotics may attack the same target, for example, an enzyme within a bacterium. If the target within the bacterium mutates, or is changed, resistance against several antibiotics may occur.

Salmonella is one such multi-resistant organism. A report by British scientists on multiple drug resistance in salmonellaes in England and Wales found that the incidence of, for example, multi-resistant salmonellae typhimurium from humans more than doubled during the years 1981 to 1988 and increased by another 7 per cent in the following two years. During the same period the incidence of multi-resistant salmonellae typhimurium from cattle quadrupled (81). One cause for this was the continuing use of a range of various antibiotics in calf husbandry (82). Similarly, in Holland up to 80 per cent of certain kinds of salmonella bacteria are resistant. In contrast, in Sweden where antibiotic use in feed additives has been banned since 1986 and where a comprehensive Salmonella eradication programme has been followed for the last 30 years, the percentage of salmonella typhimurium resistant to a range of antibiotics is very low (83).

Similar links have been suggested between other multi-resistant bacteria and the use of antibiotics, for example, between campylobacter whose resistance to antibiotics coincides with the increasing use of fluoroquinolones in human and veterinary medicine. In Holland, the numbers of campylobacter in poultry products that were found to be resistant to the antibiotic quinolone increased from 0 to 14 per cent between 1982 and 1989 while resistance in humans increased from 0 to 11 per cent (84).

The use of antibiotics in animal production is seen as being potentially harmful for humans in a number of different ways. First, resistance in animals means that multi-resistant diseases may be passed on to humans via close contact with farm animals or transmission through undercooked food. There is also a concern that residues in food might be responsible for hypersensitising reactions to antibiotics in humans (85). Second, there is concern over transmission of resistance between unrelated bacteria species. Under laboratory conditions it has been possible to transmit vancomycin resistance from enterococci to staphylococcus aureus bacteria (86). As a result, there is concern that resistant bacteria in animals could begin to share their immunity with other bacteria which infect people.

In Denmark, for example, enterococcus has become resistant to the animal antibiotic avoparcin which is often used in pig and poultry feed. The bacteria shares its resistance with other bacteria, for example staphylococci found in abundance in hospitals. Vancomycin is one of two medicines which can still be used against them (87). In May 1995, Denmark, following the examples of Finland and Sweden, implemented a unilateral ban on avoparcin and requested a ban on avoparcin in animal feed throughout the EU. Germany implemented a ban in January 1996. More recently Austria and the Netherlands also applied bans. In the UK 80 per cent of broiler chickens, 30 to 40 per cent of pigs and 30 per cent of dairy cows are routinely fed avoparcin in their feed. It is also used for calves and beef cattle.

After imposing their ban, the Danish authorities asked the Commission to re-examine the use of avoparcin as an additive in feedstuffs. After a nine month investigation, in August 1997 the EU Scientific Committee for Animal Nutrition ruled that they could find no conclusive evidence that the use of avoparcin could cause cross-resistance to antibiotics in both humans and animals. In January 1997, the Commission decided to adopt a ban on avoparcin as a precautionary and protective measure in 'the current climate of doubt'. The ban came into force on 1 April 1997 (88).

Concerns surrounding the risk of bacteria becoming antibiotic-resistant were first brought to public attention in the UK with an epidemic outbreak of Salmonella typhimurium associated with infected calves in the 1960s. As a result, the UK government set up the Swann Committee (1969) to examine questions raised about the use of antibiotics in animal husbandry and to determine its impact on animal and human health. It recommended that antibiotics should be excluded from animal feed:

- unless specifically prescribed for this purpose by a vet;

- if they are used as therapeutic agents in human or veterinary medicine; or

● if they are associated with the development of cross-resistance to drugs used in humans.

A major consequence of the report was a tightening up of the use of antibiotics in the UK and a strict separation of those used on animals from those used on humans, with human use having priority (89). In principle, growth-promoting antibiotics can only be licensed if they do not produce cross-resistance to antibiotics used in human therapy.

In 1991 an expert group on animal feedstuffs was set up in the UK and its findings presented in the Lamming Report (1992). This report highlighted a number of concerns about the use of antibiotics in feedstuffs. First, it highlighted the fact that misuse may be arising because many farmers still do not understand that the only veterinary medicines which may be incorporated in animal feed are those for which the product licence particularly specifies that use. Second, the group also expressed concern that antibiotic resistance may be developing in salmonella and e.coli and recommended increased monitoring. Third, they reinforced the recommendation, already applied in the UK, that antibiotics which could give cross-resistance to those used in human medicine should not be used as growth promoters. In addition, and more controversially, they also suggested that the same should be applied to antibiotics used in any prophylactic treatment (90). These recommendations were accepted by the UK government and the problem of antibiotic resistance is currently being investigated by the Advisory Committee on the Microbiological Safety of Food.

Conclusion

The problem of antibiotic-resistant bacteria is growing, making some infections in both animals and people harder to treat. This development has serious implications for public health and it is a risk that consumers cannot protect themselves from through their food choices; it is a risk to the population as a whole. Antibiotic use in animal rearing is associated with intensive farming methods which increase the susceptibility to cross-infection between animals and hence increased use of antibiotics to maintain the health of the herd. High guaranteed prices under the CAP have encouraged farmers to increase the quantity of output and hence intensification and antibiotic use. The supply-led approach to food production under the CAP may also account for the reluctance of the regulatory authorities to act to protect consumers from a serious public health risk.

6. Pesticides

Pesticides are chemical substances used in agriculture to: protect plant products against harmful organisms or prevent action from those organisms; influence the life processes of plants; prevent or destroy undesirable plants; and preserve plant products. They are grouped according to specific pest targets: herbicides, fungicides, and insecticides. They are an integral component of modern intensive agriculture, and their widespread use since the 1950s has resulted in higher productivity and yields in both crop and horticultural production. Additionally, the use of pesticides before and after harvest has contributed to the better appearance and longer shelf-life of many food products.

Consumer Concerns

Health issues relating to pesticides have, until recently, focused primarily on the risks of acute poisoning due to exposure through farm work and spray drifts. Today there is increasing concern about the possible threat to consumers from accumulation of pesticides residues in food (fruit, vegetables, milk) and in drinking water.

According to the World Resources Institute (WRI), scientific studies on animals have shown that exposure to pesticides can lead to a deterioration of the immune system impairing the body's resistance to infectious diseases and certain cancers (91). These studies, undertaken in a laboratory using a high concentration of pesticides do not reflect the exposure to chronic slow concentration, and could limit the conclusions which can be drawn from them. However, a survey undertaken by the WRI on the issue of pesticide impact on the human immune system shows a correlation between pesticide exposure and the incidence of diseases directly linked with the impairment of the immune system. The case studies are based on different agricultural areas, where both workers and local populations are exposed to high levels of pesticides, and on groups working in pesticides factories. It also includes evidence of similar impact on certain animals including sea mammals (92).

Additionally, there is increasing concern over the risks to health and reproduction linked to pesticides which are potentially disruptive to the endocrine system. Many of the commonly used pesticides fall into that category, for example, atrazine, lindane, and benomyl (93).

Scientists have highlighted the issue of possible synergistic interaction between different chemical residues, which in some cases, significantly increase their toxicity. According to an article in *Science*, if certain pesticides were combined, for example endosulfan and DDT, they became 160 to 1,600 times more oestrogenic than either pesticide alone (94).

A recent focus relates to the impact of insecticides particularly organo-phosphates, on the central nervous system and the brain. Children are probably the most vulnerable as the brain does not fully develop until the age of twelve.

The persistence of risks

Despite over 30 years of controls and legislation (see pages 50 and 51), the risks to human health from pesticide contamination has not significantly decreased and some even argue that while the nature of risks has changed, the levels remain high (95). The contradiction between the promotion of healthy diets rich in fruit and vegetables and the problem of increasing exposure to pesticide residues is becoming increasingly apparent. Consumer self-protection, through careful washing and peeling fruit and vegetables, is no longer ensured as residues can be increasingly found deeper inside and not just on the surface peel or skin (96).

Regulation: pesticides

In the UK, control over the use of pesticides is implemented via the 1985 Food and Environment Protection Act and the related 1986 Control of Pesticides Regulations.

The approval of a pesticide is dependent upon scientific information the manufacturer provides on short and long-term toxicity and cumulative effects. This information is assessed by MAFF's Pesticide Safety Directorate who then report to the Advisory Committee on Pesticides (ACP). Labelling of pesticides is also subject to an approval system. All approved pesticide products are subject to routine review but may be reviewed at any time if other evidence concerning its safety is provided.

The 1994 Pesticides Regulations set statutory MRLs in crops, food and feedingstuffs. A constant surveillance monitoring programme covers dietary staples such as bread, milk and potatoes and rolling annual programmes for cereals, fruit and vegetables and products of animal origin. The full results of this monitoring are published each year.

The Environment Agency monitors pesticides in water and sets Statutory Environmental Quality Standards for eight types of pesticides. The DETR has proposed values for a further 14 pesticides.

At EU level, two directives were adopted in 1986 on the fixing of MRLs for pesticide residues in and on cereals (Directive 86/362/EEC) and in and on foodstuff of animal origin (Directive 86/363/EEC). These directives stipulated that all member states must observe and enforce the maximum levels.

In 1990, Directive 90/642/EEC provided for mandatory Community MRLs on products previously not covered by Community legislation. In addition it contains rules for monitoring residues in plant products. However, the Council of Ministers retained the power to fix these levels.

In 1991, the Council Directive on Plant Protection Products 91/414/EEC was adopted setting up a legal framework to encourage harmonisation of the EU system for pesticides registration. Annex I is a positive list of active substances for which there is no evidence of toxicity on humans, animals and the environment. The Directive also established a system for the authorisation at member state level of specific formulated pesticide products in compliance with agreed criteria, 'the Uniform principles' and included a 12-year programme to evaluate the active substances on the positive list. Additionally, provision was made for harmonisation of rules on labelling and packaging. A new directive 97/41/EC makes further changes to the legislation (see page 55). It has to be brought into force by the end of 1998.

Pesticides are also covered by legislation on water quality. The 1980 EU Drinking Water Directive sets the standard for the amount of pesticide permissible in drinking water and in groundwater intended for drinking. The maximum admissible concentration (MACs) in water for any one pesticide is set at 0.1 microgramme per litre and the total sum of all pesticides in water should not exceed five times that figure. This limit applies to all member states, but they can conditionally authorise a pesticide that may not comply.

Despite the aim to reduce chemical inputs in agriculture as part of both the CAP reform and the objectives of the fifth environmental action plan, a 1996 Eurostat survey showed that pesticide use, for example, on arable crops in the UK, only fell by 7 per cent between 1992 and 1994, despite a 12 per cent reduction in plant area as a result of voluntary set-aside (97). The report also highlighted the fact that due to increased use of organophosphates, the weight of pesticides applied for the period 1992 to 1994 almost doubled. Similarly, the 1995 MAFF survey of pesticide residues in food showed, for example, higher levels of lindane residues than in previous years with approximately 5 per cent of samples proving to be above the permitted maximum residue level (MRL) (98). Many pesticides, used in excess of 5000 tonnes each year, are classified as probable or transient leachers to waters. Data collected in 1994 showed that the pesticides atrazine, mecopropo and diuron were detected above 0.1 microgramme per litre in fresh surface water and isoproturon, diuron, mecopropo and bentazone above 0.1 microgramme per litre in groundwater (99).

Residues in products such as fruit and vegetables, cereals and milk and in drinking water have been increasingly reported to have breached permissible levels (100). A Finnish customs food inspector declared in 1996 that one in ten shipments of fruit and vegetables imported from the European Union (EU) was not up to EU standards. Processed goods were also highlighted as a problem area (101).

On a more positive note, the 1994 report of the UK drinking water inspectorate showed an improvement in the overall quality of drinking water and increased compliance with MRLs. In spite of this, however, more water supply zones failed to comply with standards for individual pesticides. Furthermore, herbicides, and especially those used in cereal production, are increasingly found in groundwater (102).

The problem of pesticide residues has been exacerbated by the fact that certain pesticides have proved to be very persistent in the environment. Despite severe restrictions, many older chemicals such as the insecticides lindane and dieldrin are still found in relatively high concentrations in groundwater. In addition, while current approval procedures for any new active substance require exacting toxicological tests and are generally seen to be relatively stringent and rigorously applied, there are concerns that many old pesticides still in use were released on the market many years ago without similar investigation standards. Systematic re-evaluation of old active substances, which in some cases have been on the market for the last 40 years, is only just being introduced at EU level.

The MRLs directives have been criticised for their optionality and the laborious procedure involved in the Council fixing maximum levels on proposals from the Commission. Until 1992 only five separate proposals were adopted establishing MRLs for only 70 of the 700 substances concerned. MRLs do not represent safety limits but indicate the highest levels of residues that should be in foods when pesticides are applied correctly. On the other hand acceptable daily intake (ADI) of a particular residue expresses a safety margin. There has been some concern that to date ADIs have based their criteria on normal adults and not on more vulnerable sections of the population such as babies, children, and elderly or chronically ill people.

When EU drinking water standards were introduced in 1980, they represented, to a certain extent, the inclusion of the precautionary principle in legislation. Today, however, there is increasing concern over the safety margins of maximum acceptable concentrations (MACs) which are set at the same level for all types of pesticides and so do not necessarily take into account the different toxicological effects of individual substances.

According to EU legislation on water quality, the overall sum of different pesticide residues in water must not exceed 0.5 microgrammes per litre. This standard applies to all combinations of pesticides. However, both the WRI and the Pesticide Trust highlight the implications of chemical synergistic reactions which could be significantly more hazardous than the sum of toxicity levels for individual pesticides. The problems surrounding combinations of different pesticides in drinking water and food products is particularly important when addressing the overall safety standards applied to individual pesticides. Additionally, there is concern about the toxicity of degradation products or metabolites of certain pesticides which in some cases can be higher than the parent product at the same concentration.

The increasing incidence of pesticides in drinking water has incurred considerable costs as a result of the need for increased monitoring of food and water and the necessary cleaning-up process. According to the Pesticide Trust, the capital cost to consumers in the UK of treating pesticide-polluted water is estimated at £800 million and the annual running costs amount to approximately £80 million. In addition to polluted water the increasing problem linked with intensive pesticides use has been the resistance which many pest targets develop to chemicals applied. The build-up of resistance in pest population leads farmers to increase the levels of chemicals applied, thereby exacerbating problems of pest mismanagement. This is increasingly known as the 'pesticide treadmill' (103). In the UK, resistance action groups involving the Pesticides Safety Directorate, research institutes and the industry have been set up to try to tackle these problems by providing better information and advice to farmers.

In addition, the trend in pest resistance to chemicals coupled with restrictions on permissible residues has given rise to the development of very potent, low-dose-per-treated area pesticides. Serious implications are thought to be linked with such new substances. First, their use has been associated with an exacerbation of the already serious issue of pesticide resistance and secondary pest problems. Second, these chemicals used in such low quantities are very difficult to detect in water and in food products making the assessment of their toxicological profile as well as the monitoring of their presence, increasingly difficult (104).

The Commission has adopted a new directive on MRLs which will result in several changes to the framework legislation for MRLs in the EU (105). First, the authority for agreeing amendments to the MRLs will transfer from the Agriculture Council to the Commission Standing Committee on Plant Health. This is supposed to enable changes to MRLs to be made more quickly. Second, the scope of the current pesticide residues directive will be extended to processed and composite products (except for baby foods, where special provisions apply). In the case of baby foods, the Commission is to forward proposals to the Council to establish specific contaminant limits for baby and infant foods by January 1999. These levels will be agreed by the Standing Committee for Foodstuffs. Third, the Commission will be charged with recommending harmonised residue monitoring programmes to member states and has been given the responsibility of preparing EU summary reports for residue monitoring results which member states supply to them. The directive must be brought into force by 31 December 1998.

Conclusion

Pesticides are an integral component of western intensive agriculture and the CAP's high support prices have given additional encouragement to their use. The regulatory system has been slow to react to the safety concerns that have been identified. While new substances are subject to a relatively stringent testing programme, the systematic re-evaluation of other pesticides is only recently being introduced at EU level. Progress on the adoption of MRLs has been slow and their monitoring inadequate.

7. Fertilisers and the nitrate problem

Plants need nitrogen, which is found naturally in the soil, in order to make the proteins necessary for plant growth. However, efforts to increase the amount of production that can be achieved on the same area of land have led to the increased use of fertilisers. Fertilisers are differentiated between manufactured inorganic chemicals and natural organic substances. Both are spread and mixed with soil to make it richer and promote plant growth. If input is excessive, however, residues can accumulate in agricultural produce and/or nitrate can leach into surface or ground water supplies.

Consumer Concerns

Nitrates, as such, are not perceived to be dangerous to human health. In fact, most adults can temporarily tolerate high quantities before suffering any adverse effects. However, health risks from nitrates are thought to occur as a result of bacterial action in the mouth which transforms nitrates into nitrites which pose a greater threat to human health. For most adults only 5 per cent of nitrates undergo this transformation. In new-born babies, however, this proportion can reach 80 per cent, which can give rise to a condition called methaemoglobineamia otherwise known as 'blue baby' syndrome. This is a rare disease affecting oxygen transport in the body and only affects bottle-fed babies. In the cases of adults, nitrites are dangerous when they combine with amino acids in the stomach to produce nitrosamines. There is evidence that nitrosamines are carcinogenic.

The health concerns of consumers focus on the risks to human health from high levels of nitrate residues found in agricultural produce, particularly fruit and vegetables, and from contamination of drinking water.

Nitrate residues in agricultural produce

Fears surrounding nitrate residues in agricultural produce are focused primarily on residues in vegetables. In particular, there is concern about the consumption of those vegetables which have a tendency to take up and retain large amounts of nitrates. Consumers also need to be aware of the seasonal variation of nitrate levels in vegetables which tend to increase over the winter months. A study in Belgium found that, given the current levels of nitrate residues found in vegetables, on average the daily consumption per individual was 80 per cent of the recommended daily intake (106). However, once this was converted into nitrites, consumption was 112 per cent of the recommended daily intake. In an analysis of daily diet it was found that products with low levels of nitrates but consumed in larger quantities proved to be more important in increasing the average daily intake of nitrates. It is important therefore to reduce nitrate residue levels in all vegetables, both those high in take-up of nitrates, as well as those that have only low levels, in order to reduce consumers' overall daily intake of nitrates. Not surprisingly vegetarians are likely to consume greater levels of nitrates.

However, although a number of studies have shown nitrosamines to be carcinogenic, several other epidemiological studies have shown that among large consumers of fruit and vegetables, there is, in fact, a lower incidence of stomach cancer (107). This could mean that the harmful impact of nitrosamines is neutralised by 'protection' factors such as fibre and the vitamins C and E found in fruit and vegetables (108). As yet, however, there is still considerable uncertainty about the risk associated with a diet high in nitrates and, as a result, most European Union (EU) countries set maximum authorised levels of nitrate residues for a number of vegetables.

In the light of the European Commission's proposal (since introduced) for maximum permitted limits of nitrate residues in vegetables, MAFF initiated a surveillance project to update the surveillance data on nitrate concentrations in vegetables. The nitrate limits proposed by the Commission are set out in table 3.

The Food Surveillance Unit's report of July 1996 showed some worrying statistics. The percentage of lettuce samples that exceeded the proposed limits of 4500mg/kg during the winter period were 3 per cent in December and February but rose to 14 per cent in January. Mean nitrate concentration indicated that loose leafed hearted lettuce types, such as round and curly lettuce, contained more nitrate than compact leafed hearted types. For spinach the percentage of samples found to be above the winter limit of 3000mg/kg fresh product was found to be 15 per cent. In August 46 per cent were found to be above the summer limit.

Table 3 Nitrate limits in proposed EC Regulation 3080/93

Vegetable	Harvest period	Maximum nitrate content (mg of nitrate per kg of fresh product)
Spinach	(From 1/7/96 to 31/12/98)	
	1 November to 31 March	3000
	1 April to 31 October	2500
	From January 1999	2500
Preserved/frozen		(processed product) 2000
Lettuce	(From 1996)	
	1 November to 31 March	4500
	1 April to 31 October	3500
Outdoor lettuce	1 May to 31 August	2500

Source: Food Surveillance Unit, MAFF, 1994.

Overall more than 25 per cent of samples from the UK crop exceeded the proposed limit. More worrying for consumers was the degree to which samples exceeded those limits. The nitrate concentration for spinach between October and December was reported as being between 33 to 60 per cent above the Commission's proposed safety limits (109). In a recent study by Test Santé in Belgium on average 18 per cent of lettuce were found to exceed the Belgian maximum authorised levels which are set at the lower figure of 4000mg/kg.

Contamination of water supplies

The problem of nitrate residues, particularly in water supplies, has been a long-standing public concern in the UK. Over twenty years ago, in January 1974, the Advisory Council for Agriculture and Horticulture in England and Wales published its first report into pollution from farm waste. This report was the result of an enquiry set up to examine the role of agriculture in contributing to nitrate pollution of ground water, evidence of which had been mounting since the late 1950s.

Agriculture is seen as the primary source of nitrate pollution due to the changes in agricultural practice during the last 40 years. The steady increase in the use of chemical fertilisers is perceived to be a particularly significant factor, although the relationship between the rate of nitrogen applied and overall pollution is not always clear since it is also influenced by natural conditions such as soil types, geology, topology and climate. However, the specialisation and concentration of intensive production at regional and farm levels has aggravated the problem of nitrate pollution, particularly in areas with a high concentration of livestock where organic manure is a major source of pollution (110).

Nitrate in water above certain concentrations can be a danger to human health. Unlike the problem of nitrate residues found in vegetable produce there are no potential 'protection' factors such as vitamins and fibre which may ameliorate the effects of the residues. This suggests that there is a greater threat from nitrate residues in water than from comparative residues in food produce. The directive on the quality of drinking water includes 62 standards for the quality of water to protect human health (111). The maximum standard for nitrates is set at 50mg per litre based on the safety threshold set by the World Health Organisation (WHO) but, within the EU, water intended for human consumption is supposed to meet a guide level of 25mg per litre.

However, a recent report by the European Environment Agency shows a serious decline in ground water quality (112). The result of their monitoring suggests that 85 per cent of the agricultural area in Europe has nitrate levels above the guide level and 20 per cent exceeds the maximum admissible level set by the EU.

The Nitrate Directive

The EU has sought to address the problem of nitrates in water through the so-called Nitrate Directive which forms the cornerstone of present EU nitrate policy in respect to agriculture (113). Its overall objective is to reduce and prevent water pollution caused or induced by nitrates from agriculture. The directive provides guidance on how and when member states should deal with the nitrate problem, including regulations on how to handle manure and chemical fertilisers in vulnerable zones. It also requires an action programme for each member state.

Application of the nitrate directive rules has been extremely variable across the EU. In the UK, for example, legislation concerning spreading practice is only imposed in a very limited area designated under the Nitrate Sensitive Areas (NSAs) Scheme where the only rule is a ban on spreading near water courses, springs and wells. Most other countries have much broader regulations which include a ban on spreading throughout the country during certain winter periods. Similarly the codes of good agricultural practice that have been introduced in the UK are not as comprehensive as those prescribed in the directive.

With the various national programmes consisting of an extensive number of rules of a quite different nature the full impact on farming practice and the resulting contamination of water is difficult to assess (114). The extent to which farmers are complying with the standards in such programmes has been called into question especially since some of the rules – such as those governing how fertilisers must be spread – are difficult, if not impossible, to monitor. The question of how closely the standards are followed depends on the national authorities' enthusiasm for controlling farmers (115). There are criticisms that without effective monitoring, enforcement and controls, the mere existence of a nitrate policy will not serve to decrease levels of water contamination.

With the continuing serious decline in water quality, the Commission has adopted a policy outlining the structure of a future framework directive on water resources which aims to ensure better integration, consistency and transparency of Community water policy (116). The framework emphasises the importance of developing an integrated approach to groundwater protection. In relation to the protection of water against pollution caused by nitrates from agricultural sources, the implementation of the Nitrate Directive is still seen as the major element of any future action.

Conclusion

The overuse of nitrates and the water pollution and high residues in some vegetables that have resulted from it, is linked to the high support prices of the CAP. The voluntary approach of the nitrates directive and its poor implementation demonstrate the pervasive influence of the output-oriented CAP regime. Reductions in nitrate contamination are unlikely to come about without fundamental reform of the CAP.

8. The application of biotechnology

Biotechnology is the use of any biological organism, system or process in manufacturing or in services. It has a long tradition of application in making breads and cheeses, and in fermenting wine and beer, silage and plant compost. Similarly the selective breeding of animals and plants (but not people) has been accepted without qualms, although it has changed the face of the world. The discovery of the structure of DNA allowed a revolution in our ability to control the genetic make-up of organisms and their use in traditional and new biotechnologies. The novel techniques are called 'genetic engineering', 'genetic manipulation' or 'modification' (GM), 'molecular biology' or just 'biotechnology' (with the 'new' implied). In the current context these terms have the same meaning.

The new techniques allow a single gene, chosen because it controls a characteristic that is thought desirable, to be separated by a restriction or 'scissor' enzyme. It can then be put into the plant or animal where it is expected to be useful, sometimes by means of being incorporated into a virus. These techniques allow a much wider choice of genes, which can be transferred, both within and across species, without bringing other genes that happen to be close on the chromosome with them. These are two huge advantages to the geneticist over traditional breeding techniques. A third is that genetic change can be achieved much more quickly.

Consumers concerns

The new methods of biotechnology, particularly transferring genes between distantly related organisms, pose potential new hazards. The novelty means that these techniques do not, as yet, have the track record needed for conventional risk analysis. We know that when existing plants and animals have been moved to new places unpredicted damage has been commonplace. When prickly pears and rabbits were moved to the new environment of Australia, where the existing organisms were not adapted to the imported competitors, they became spectacular pests. Traditional selective breeding has changed wild genotypes to produce the familiar breeds and varieties of plants and animals used in agriculture. As a consequence of their use on farms there have been profound ecological changes, and the genetic make-up of wild species has been altered. Genes have even been transferred between species by means of traditional genetic techniques, as in some widely used commercial wheats, and to produce mules. This has not led to unpredictable consequences, in part because the domestic varieties are unable to compete with wild species outside the farm environment, in some cases because they are sterile. This history is not, however, an adequate model for current genetic manipulation, so caution is essential.

The novelty itself causes concern among consumers and their representatives. This could lead to the rejection of products even where the benefits may far outweigh the costs. A survey done in April 1996 found that 41 per cent of consumers appeared to have some understanding of what the terms 'gene technology', 'biotechnology' or 'genetic modification' meant. Forty per cent said they were concerned about genetically modified foods, particularly the interference with nature, mentioned by 33 per cent, and the long-term consequences for the food chain and the body, mentioned by 32 per cent. Forty one per cent said they would buy food made from genetically modified plants, but only 24 per cent said that they would buy food made from genetically modified animals (117). Consumers rightly remember that changes in the feeding of cattle had unintended, but disastrous, consequences for cattle, the livelihood of farmers and almost certainly for human health. In order to be sustainable developments relying on the new biotechnologies must gain the confidence of consumers.

Regulation: biotechnology

Control in the UK has several stages. A company intending to initiate experimental work towards a GM food will need to obtain a 'contained use consent' from the Health and Safety Executive. This allows work where the organism is strictly isolated from the general environment. The next stage is a 'deliberate release consent' for planting the new crop in a field for further research. Then a marketing consent from the DETR is required for a living organism. The involvement of MAFF has been a voluntary process, since 1989, the grower being advised to apply to MAFF for approval for using the GM plant for food. This application is considered by the Advisory Committee on Novel Foods and Processes (ACNFP). Thus, for example, tomato paste made from the American GM 'flavr savr' tomato could be sold in the UK without such a consent, but the original living tomato would require a DETR marketing consent. This consent applies to the EU as a whole, and can be given only after the DETR has applied to the Commission, which consults other member states. In the UK, the need for a GM food to be labelled is assessed by the Food Advisory Committee (FAC) on a case by case basis, as part of the approval process for their use.

The deliberate release of genetically modified organisms into the environment is subject to Directive 90/220. This directive addresses environmental and human safety risks which result from deliberate release, but not when consumed as food. The directive is currently under review.

The EU only agreed measures covering the use and labelling of GM food in May 1997. In effect the Novel Foods Regulation (EC 258/97) makes something like the MAFF process compulsory, with a pre-market safety assessment from the competent authority. In the UK this is the ACNFP. Labelling of GM foods is compulsory where there is ethically sensitive material or material that may have health implications for certain sections of the population, except where the modification was made solely for agronomic reasons. Further proposals on labelling are in the pipeline (see page 70).

We and other consumer groups, have argued that manufacturers of GM foods should provide clear and accurate labelling to inform consumer choice.

The example of genetically modified soyabeans

The US company Monsanto was given approval in March 1996 to market processed genetically modified soyabean in the European Union (EU) (118). Monsanto modified 'Round-Up ready' soyabeans to be resistant to their own herbicide Round-Up. The product received approval by a qualified majority of member states, with Denmark, Sweden and Austria voting against and Luxembourg abstaining. Objections mainly concerned the potential risk that the herbicide resistance might spread, leading to weeds that would be more difficult to control. The industry claimed that in this case there would be environmental benefits as the use of herbicide could be reduced by 30 to 40 per cent.

The US exports 60 per cent of its total soyabean crop and soyabean producers are expected to plant around 1 to 2 per cent of their total crop with the genetically modified strain. Monsanto and the American Soyabean Association decided not to segregate GM soyabean from the conventional crop. So imports from the US may contain modified soya and thus foods with soya cannot be labelled as containing, or as not containing, modified soya. In the UK manufacturers and retailers have in general continued to use soya in products without being able to inform consumers on labels. Soya is used in many processed products and consumer representatives were extremely critical of the lack of segregation which denied consumers the right to choose whether to buy the GM product or not.

In Germany Nestlé and Unilever have responded to consumer pressure. They have made a commitment not to use GM soyabeans. Nestlé Deutschland uses only 2,000 tonnes of soyabeans in a year and said they could easily obtain that from sources outside the USA (119). This is a business decision and not because German law requires it. Food distributors and retailers, responding to consumer demand, are attempting to have the GM crop separated in the next season, so that consumers can choose. As so much of the worldwide market seems to have accepted an unsegregated supply the prospects for segregation are not good. A relatively small supply of soya certified to be free of the modified variety may be possible, but it would be difficult to be confident that it was genuinely so.

The example of genetically modified maize

There is widespread concern among consumer organisations about the European Commission's authorisation for the marketing of the genetically modified maize notified by Ciba-Geigy (120). The maize has three new genes. The Bt gene brings resistance to the corn borer. The second confers tolerance to a herbicide. However, the main concern is about the third gene, for antibiotic resistance, which may become incorporated into a micro-organism pathogenic to humans. This gene confers the ability to produce an enzyme, beta-lactamase, which destroys ampicillin, an antibiotic in the penicillin family.

Genes for antibiotic resistance are commonly used merely as convenient markers in the process of genetic manipulation. When a gene conferring a desired characteristic, such as immunity to attack by an insect pest, is to be transferred to a valuable plant that lacks it, it is essential to be able to pick out the very rare cells where transfer was successful from the many where it failed. If the gene is closely associated with another that gives resistance to, say, ampicillin, then only those cells that the experimenter wants will grow in an environment having ampicillin. There is no problem about the contained use of this system for laboratory research but antibiotic resistance is already a severe medical problem, and it will probably become more so (see chapter 5). The use of the antibiotic resistance in maize that is released into the general environment carries a small risk that it may add to the problem, thus making the control of disease needlessly difficult.

The Environment Council of Ministers of 25 June 1996 drew no conclusion on the application, although seven member states (including the UK) had raised various objections. The responsibility for a decision therefore returned to the Commission, who took advice from three committees, and then allowed the application. Their reports advised that:

- The use of Bt-maize in human food will not adversely affect human health because the gene for resistance to the antibiotic will have been broken down into fragments smaller than the relevant gene;

- It will not harm animal health unacceptably from its use in animal feed; and

- A potential development of insect resistance to the Bt toxin cannot be considered an adverse environmental effect as existing agricultural means of control of insects will still be available.

This advice is not adequate, however. Consumers will not only consume the processed maize direct; they will also consume the unprocessed meat of animals fed with unprocessed GM maize. It does not follow that there is no risk to human health from Bt-maize, unprocessed, in animal feed.

The issues raised in cases of this kind were analysed by the UK's Advisory Committee on Novel Foods and Processes (ACNFP) (121). The ACNFP came down against accepting the general use of antibiotic-resistant marker genes in

GM micro-organisms consumed live by people or animals because of the potential risk that resistance might spread to other, pathogenic, micro-organisms. They write 'It is considered that some of the DNA in fresh and ensiled plant material is likely to be intact and that the probability of transfer of an antibiotic resistance marker to rumen micro-organisms would increase with increasing exposure; ..... Although the probability at any time is low, it is not zero, and, given time enough transfer may occur, with the risk to human health that would follow'. The ACNFP recommended rejection of Ciba-Geigy's GM maize on the grounds that it could be a hazard for the future use of penicillins. The UK Government accepted its evidence.

The ACNFP pointed out that it would be possible to use alternative, if less convenient, markers, or to remove an antibiotic resistant marker after it was used. Indeed this has now been done, and four new types of GM maize have just been approved by MAFF (122).

Although the Commission has given its authorisation, the governments of Austria, Luxembourg and Italy have refused to allow GM maize to be imported into their countries saying that it poses a threat to human health. In September 1997 the Commission called on these countries to reverse their ban but no further action has been taken (123).

There has been much criticism of the EU regulatory framework and the directive on the release of genetically modified organisms is currently under review (124). Concerns include the lack of clarity over which products fall under the directive, and the fact that a risk assessment can currently be carried out based on different criteria in different member states.

The EU has also adopted a set of guidelines to serve as a basis for drawing up formal draft proposals which will require obligatory labelling rules for products that may contain genetically modified organisms (GMOs). Producers will also be able to label their foodstuffs 'GMO free' as part of a positive labelling campaign. GMO labelling laws will also cover seed and feedstuffs. Soya and maize products are the first products to be covered by GMO labelling legislation (125).

In November 1997, food manufacturers and retailers in the UK announced a voluntary agreement to label food containing genetically modified protein when it appeared in supermarkets and shops from January 1998. However, the Food and Drink Federation which represents manufacturers has called for European-wide legislation to ensure that different labelling between countries does not confuse consumers (126).

However, in the maize case discussed above labelling would not help consumers (although they should be informed as a matter of principle), as the health risk is to the whole population rather than to the individual. No choice at the time of purchase would offer protection from antibiotic resistance among bacteria in our common environment.

If consumers are to accept the techniques of biotechnology then they will need to be convinced that they are appropriately regulated and that genetic modification can be of benefit to them. Some issues that might be addressed are:

- the development of safer methods of pest control in agriculture, by appropriate manipulation of farmed crops and animals, or of organisms used for biological control. (The biotechnological creation of pesticide resistance could, however, have the opposite effect);

- improvements in the micronutrient content of food;

- products to help treat or prevent disease. Work is being undertaken at the Institute of Food Research to improve the antioxidant and cancer inhibiting composition of brassicas. (However, as some plant substances that may inhibit cancer development evolved in plants for defence against herbivores, safety will have to be monitored carefully);

- the development of crops and animals able to cope in warmer and more variable climates; and

- the development of foods for people with special dietary needs.

Conclusion

The new biotechnology, genetic modification, raises a number of concerns for consumers. As with any new technology, there are risks, and the benefits are not at all obvious as there are, as yet, only a few products available at the consumer end of the food chain. The novelty of the technology means that it does not yet have the track record needed for conventional risk analysis. The development of the regulatory system in Europe has lagged behind the development of the technology and is still flawed. It is essential that the development and regulation of genetically modified foods does not take the traditional supply-led approach to food production.

9. A new direction for agricultural policy

The agricultural support policy of the CAP has effectively separated agriculture from the stringencies of the open market. Instead of the interaction of consumer demand and farmer supply deciding the price, quantity and quality of food agriculture ministers from each of the member states meet each year to fix the prices that farmers will receive for their produce. As a result, it is the CAP that largely determines the nature and level of agricultural production in Europe.

The CAP is a very expensive policy for consumers. Although the burden of support has shifted towards taxpayers with the MacSharry reforms, the costs to consumers remain significant – an estimated 39 billion ECU in 1996. In addition, the CAP objectives do not include any consideration of the health or nutritional needs of Europe's consumers, or of consumer choice. With its preoccupation with maintaining farm incomes, the CAP has focused on the supply side of the economic equation rather than on consumer demand. This has led to, for example, consumers being denied access to certain healthy cheap foods as products are withdrawn from the market in order to keep prices high.

Also, in an attempt to maintain farm incomes through the blunt instrument of price support, the CAP has encouraged greater farm output with little concern for overall product quality. Quite apart from the concern for consumers' health due to, for example, chemical residues in food, it has been argued that through encouraging intensive farming methods, without any corresponding quality requirements, the CAP has also been the cause of a lowering in the quality of produce being offered to consumers (127). Where quality standards exist they tend to be supply-led. Tomatoes, for instance, are graded in terms of appearance, uniformity and ability to 'withstand transport and handling'.

Criteria for water content and flavour, or conformity with maximum residue levels or pesticides, are noticeable by their absence. The policies followed under the CAP tend to undermine the quality of produce offered to consumers.

Intensive farming and the consumer interest

Although, in keeping with other industries, a modernisation and rationalisation of agricultural practice has been inevitable over the last fifty years, the high level of farming intensification has been exacerbated by the mechanisms of the CAP. Farmers have sought to maximise production in response to the high guaranteed prices which have been unrelated to quality or consumer health criteria. The use of hormones or antibiotics as growth promoters and the level of use of pesticides and fertilisers have been encouraged by an all-out approach to increasing production. Until the MacSharry reforms attempts to control the massive over-production that resulted have been based on quantity controls, rather than price cuts, so incentives to farmers have remained distorted.

Consumers are questioning the use of these production methods. For example, many consumer groups argue that the use of antibiotics is greater than it need be because of current animal production methods. These methods increase the susceptibility of cross-infection between animals and as a result require additional medical intervention through the use of antibiotics in order to maintain the herd's health. Antibiotics are being used to counter the effects of intensive rearing methods, or as a substitute for good animal husbandry. It is argued, for example, that the additional marginal growth rates achieved by adding antibiotics to the feed of otherwise healthy animals compensates for the impairment of growth rate caused by high stocking densities (128). In addition, intensive production has blurred the dividing lines between the use of antibiotics for therapy, disease prevention, and growth promotion. Under the high stocking densities of intensive systems if one animal is ill it is likely that it will infect the rest of the herd. It is argued, therefore, that it is prudent to apply antibiotics, as a preventive measure, to all the herd, whether infected or not.

In Sweden, where there has been a ban on additives in feedstuffs since 1986, the national farmers' organisation – the Swedish Farmers' Association – has demonstrated that an acceptable growth rate can be achieved in animals without the use of antibiotics and without adversely affecting the economic viability of production (129). To decrease the use of antibiotics the Swedish Farmers' Association suggests changes in production systems and improvements in rearing conditions to improve overall animal health. These include:

- reducing the overall stocking rates and intensity;

- improving the design and hygiene standards of animal housing;

- breeding programmes aimed at promoting healthier animals and resistance to disease;

- developing feeds and feeding systems that promote good animal health;

- better attention to hygiene all along the food production chain. This would include improved conditions in transportation and at livestock markets; and

- increased supervision so that breeders are kept from moving sick animals between different markets.

The BSE crisis exemplifies the problems created by the drive for quantity over quality and demonstrates the link between the various problems surrounding intensive agricultural processes. For example, in order to avoid the spread of BSE, the European Union (EU) banned the use of animal remains in feed for cattle and sheep, so it was replaced with intensively produced vegetable produce. Subsequently, there has been an increase in the levels of pesticide residues, notably lindane in milk (130). Such examples demonstrate the pervasiveness of the problems associated with intensive farming, where correcting the symptoms, without tackling the root cause, leads to problems in other areas.

Better models

As long as price support remains the dominant feature of the CAP farmers will clearly continue to use intensive production methods with high levels of farm inputs, and concentrate on quantity rather than quality. A high level of overall price support and, specifically, high prices for particular commodities promote a concentration on intensive production of one commodity. There is little incentive to aim for a higher quality product that may, in practice, lead to lower output. This undermines the benefits of less intensive farming practices. Similarly there is little encouragement for the realisation of joint economies of scale from mixed farming practices which incorporate crop rotations to reduce the risk of pests and plant disease and to increase soil fertility.

However, some member states are adapting their agricultural production processes to meet the increasing consumer demands for quality and safety. There are also some signs that the European Commission itself is taking such demands seriously.

In Sweden, for example, the Swedish Farmers' Association devised a consumer policy programme which was adopted by the Swedish Government in 1992. This 'On Our Way' programme aims to increase Swedish people's confidence in, and preference for, Swedish food and raw materials. The scheme is voluntary and relies largely on a broad education and advisory initiative for farmers although, in certain geographically sensitive areas, a regulatory approach to farm inputs has been adopted. The programme has sought to extensify production by, for example, encouraging the reintroduction of 'traditional' agricultural practices such as crop rotation in order to reduce reliance on pesticides and fertilisers. In addition, in 1996 the government promoted the idea of environmental inspections for each farm to evaluate and subsequently reduce their use of farm inputs. Each county has an advisor who supports farmers through advice and encouragement in undertaking such a survey.

The policy is promoted to farmers in terms of the savings they can make by using their farm inputs more efficiently but also in terms of creating a better image for Swedish products which can then subsequently be marketed more effectively. This policy has led to a 50 per cent drop in nitrogen use, an 80 per cent reduction in cadmium from phosphorus fertilisers and a 70 per cent drop in pesticide use since 1985 (131). In the latter the biggest area of decrease has been in the use of weed killers in grain fields through changing the perceptions of farmers, built up over the last forty years, that fields have to be completely free of weeds or pests in order to achieve efficiency. Such perceptions have contributed to the overuse of pesticides and fertilisers. As described above, the Swedes have also banned the use of antibiotics as growth promoters which has led to a 35 per cent reduction in the overall use of antibiotics (132). The assumption underpinning such reductions is that good animal and plant husbandry, set within a less intensive production system, rectifies any problems at source rather than attempting to cure the symptoms (133).

Both Denmark and Austria have adopted similar if less well-developed schemes. As a result, Denmark, for example, achieved a fall in consumption of pesticides by 18 per cent between 1986 and 1991 (134).

In recent years the EU has shifted away from a policy of production at any cost. Since 1987 modest sums of money have been available for extensification of agricultural production although by 1995 only 300,000 hectares were affected by the scheme across the EU (135). The 1992 MacSharry reforms, while heavily flawed in the attempt to decouple the support of farm incomes from food production, have signalled a desire to move away from the massive overproduction of the 1970s and 1980s.

The European Commission officially recognised organic farming at European level and supplemented their rules on it in 1992 and 1993 and in the recent proposal of 1996 (136). As a result money can be allocated to support organic farming which is defined according to Community rules as a system of managing agricultural holdings that implies major restrictions on fertilisers and pesticides (137). The method of production is based on varied crop farming practices and avoids chemical pesticides and fertilisers. Inspections are carried out at all stages of production and marketing, with a compulsory product labelling scheme. These are officially recognised and supervised by each member state, involving regular checks on all operators. By 1993 405,500 hectares were under organic schemes in the EU. Currently the organic scheme only covers arable production and the Commission is now finalising the preparation of a proposal to extend its scope to animal production. However, although looking favourably at organic agriculture, the Commission sees it as representing only 2.5 per cent of agricultural sales by the year 2000 (138).

Organic production usually entails higher prices. However, not all consumers wish, or can afford, to pay the premium necessary to get organic food, yet a large majority would like reduced chemical use on mainstream supplies. As a result, while recognition of organic farming is important in providing consumers with additional choice it is only likely to be successful in satisfying a small sector of the market.

Agenda 2000

In July 1997 the Commission published further proposals for reform of the CAP. These continue the process, established in the 1992 MacSharry reforms, of reducing support prices and moving to direct payments to compensate farmers for the price cuts. As with the MacSharry reforms, the Agenda 2000 proposals concentrate on the cereals and beef sectors with very limited reforms proposed for dairy products.

We welcome the proposed cut in the support price for cereals which should lead to lower prices further down the food chain, and discourage the use of expensive inputs. It is estimated, for example, that a reduction in cereal prices of 30 per cent would lead to an 11 per cent fall in nitrogen use (139). The proposal for a non-crop specific compensation payment is an improvement as it will encourage farmers to respond to market signals rather than different subsidy levels for different products.

However, the direct payments remain compensation payments, and are not fully decoupled from production. Compensation payments for reductions in price support can only be justified for a short transition period during which they should be steadily reduced. The proposals make no mention of time limits or phased reductions. There is a proposal to introduce individual farm ceilings on payments and to allow member states to apply 'differentiation' criteria. These may have a role in the transition from compensation payments to fully decoupled direct payments. However, they are unacceptable as a permanent support mechanism as they perpetuate payments for compensation.

The compensation payments should be replaced by fully decoupled direct payments designed to meet specific environmental, social or regional development needs. We particularly favour environmental management payments which would reward farmers for providing environmental services which society values rather than compensate them for past excessive subsidies. They could also have a positive impact on the quality and safety of food for consumers through reductions in chemical inputs. The proposal to allow member states to add environmental provisions if they so wish is insufficient and highly unlikely to be effective.

The proposed 30 per cent price cut for beef is welcome but is unlikely to be sufficient to prevent overproduction. The compensation payments appear high and unfortunately, as with cereals, they are not time-limited nor are there any plans to gradually reduce them. The dairy proposals are most disappointing. Quotas are to be retained and the proposed 10 per cent price cut will not be sufficient to prevent the build-up of surpluses even on the Commission's optimistic assumptions.

While the preamble to the proposals includes welcome recognition of the importance of food safety and quality, these do not feature at all in the proposals themselves. As with the MacSharry proposals environmental measures, to the extent they exist at all, are tacked on to payments designed primarily to control over-production. The production-led approach to agricultural policy is maintained.

The Agenda 2000 proposals do not sufficiently prepare the EU for enlargement to take in the Central and East European countries (CEECs). If prices in the CEECs were aligned with current high CAP support prices it would place an unreasonable burden on their consumers. Higher food prices would further reduce their already low standard of living. It would also place a large burden on EU taxpayers. Production in the CEECs is likely to increase as the structural reforms of transition to market-based economies become settled. High CAP support prices would lead to considerable surpluses which could not be exported without subsidy. If CAP direct payments were also available to CEE farmers the cost would be prohibitive.

The international dimension also has to be considered. Additional subsidised exports are likely to breach the EU's commitments on the volume and value of subsidised exports under the Uruguay Round agriculture agreement leaving the EU open to challenge in the World Trade Organisation (WTO). Also, after the so called peace clause expires in 2003, WTO member countries will be able to take action to protect their markets from the damaging impact of others' dumped exports. Negotiations in the WTO to further reduce trade distorting agricultural subsidies are due to start at the end of 1999. CAP reform proposals need to conform to the existing agreement and recognise the forthcoming agenda.

The way forward

It is important that the EU signals a new direction to farmers emphasising product quality and above all a concern for consumer health. An advisory programme throughout the EU, along similar lines to that promoted in Sweden, would be an important step in the right direction. However, such a programme will only be successful if it is operated in tandem with a reform of the whole agricultural policy structure and with a reduction in the incentives to continue intensifying production. If not, few farmers are likely to reduce inputs voluntarily when the bulk of agricultural support is encouraging them in the opposite direction.

Although it is always important to develop more efficient production methods it is essential that these are sustainable, and meet the criteria of greater consumer safety and improved product quality giving the consumer greater choice. This may require new research priorities looking to develop new production methods and technologies which reduce the use of intensive agricultural practices while improving food quality. Not enough attention is being paid to these consumer interests under the current, politically regulated, market of the CAP.

At the moment, for example, while consumers would prefer food with lower chemical residues, there is a research bias towards products that can be patented and sold, rather than towards techniques which could reduce the need for agri-chemicals. The development and promulgation of techniques such as integrated pest management may be important in discouraging the inappropriate use of pesticides.

A shift away from price support and quantity controls, as we have long recommended, will enable the market to operate, and reduce the incentive to use the expensive inputs associated with intensive production. Money saved on price policy could be used not only to finance direct payments to meet social, environmental and rural development needs, but also to fund advisory programmes, and research into safer production methods. Such measures, together with reform of the culture and substance of regulation discussed in the next chapter, would enable the EU to meet its consumers' needs as well as providing a more sustainable agricultural and rural development policy.

Recommendations

Changing incentive systems

Recommendation 1: The European Union should go much further in its reforms of the CAP. The Council of Ministers should adopt a programme of sustained cuts in support prices until they are in line with realistic world market levels. At the same time, it should phase out quantity restrictions, such as quotas, along with export refunds, and reduce import levies. Such a shift in policy would reduce farmers' incentives to intensify production. In addition, it would enhance the responsiveness of farmers to advisory programmes which seek to reduce the use of agricultural practices that may be harmful to consumer health.

Recommendation 2: The Council of Ministers should phase out compensation payments and replace them with fully 'decoupled' direct payments in particular, environmental management payments, which could also have a positive impact on the quality and safety of food. Individual farm ceilings and/or differentiation criteria may have a role in the transition from compensation payments but would have no reference to 'decoupled' direct payments which would be targeted to meet environmental, social or rural development needs.

Advisory programmes

Recommendation 3: The Council of Ministers should agree to establish and provide funding for advisory programmes which encourage farmers to adopt production methods that enhance the quality of their produce and reduce the use of antibiotics, pesticides and nitrates. This may take the form of, for example, environmental audits which help farmers to identify and reduce their use of agricultural inputs. Such a programme should also address the curricula of universities and colleges who will be training the next generation of farmers.

Research and development

Recommendation 4: Much of current agricultural research and development is biased towards products that can be patented and sold rather than towards the development and promulgation of new techniques that could reduce the need for agricultural chemicals. The European Commission should fund research and development of less intensive farming methods with a focus on improving agricultural efficiency and the quality of food.

10. Reform of regulation

The supply-dominated approach to food production encouraged by the CAP has pervaded the culture of regulation at both UK and European Union (EU) level. This has in some instances led to a lack of precaution in the licensing of products and processes – animal feed, antibiotics, GM maize – and a lack of monitoring and enforcement of regulations introduced – BSE, hormones, and residues of antibiotics, pesticides and nitrates. Consumers have lost trust in the regulatory authorities because they have paid insufficient attention to consumer protection. It is high time that a demand-led, rather than supply-led, approach is adopted.

Following criticisms of the regulatory authorities in the UK and EU over the handling of the BSE crisis, policy-makers recognised the need for reform. In February 1997 the European Commission president Jacques Santer announced a series of changes to the way in which food safety and public health issues are handled by the Commission. These provide a much greater role for the Consumer Policy and Public Heath Directorate (DC XXIV) (see appendix 2). Similarly, after the UK election in May, the new government announced its intention to establish an independent food standards agency and a white paper was published in January 1998 (see appendix 2). While both sets of reforms are more limited than consumer groups have been advocating they are welcome developments for consumers. It remains to be seen whether they will lead to a much needed change in approach.

Science, uncertainty and risk

The EU has a rigorous scientific testing programme for agricultural inputs that are subsequently marketed. However, 'safety' in relation to scientific assessment is about probabilities and not certainties. There are two kinds of uncertainty. First is risk, which is an event with a known probability (such as dying in a road accident). Second, there is true uncertainty, which is an event with unknown probability. Many health and safety issues relating to food which the regulatory system has to address involve true uncertainty. There has been insufficient experience of the product or process to provide the information about the probability of harm, for example, the products of GM technology.

To deal with 'risk' uncertainty, policy-makers have developed a process called 'risk assessment', which is useful when the probability of an outcome is known from experience. However, if conventional risk assessment is applied to problems characterised by true uncertainty it can quickly turn into guess work. The precautionary principle or approach has been developed to deal with such situations.

The precautionary principle

The precautionary principle has been developed mainly to deal with environmental problems which also tend to be characterised by 'true' uncertainty. It now appears in several international treaties on the environment. It also appears in the 1992 Treaty of the European Union at Article 130r, which explicitly includes the objective of protecting human health. Although the precautionary principle has many definitions and interpretations its main thrust is that where an activity raises potentially serious threats of harm to the environment or human health, precautionary measures should be taken even if certain cause and effect relationships are not established scientifically. There has been concern that policy-makers in Europe have not always adhered to this principle.

In the case of BSE there was an eight year gap between the emergence of the first concerns about public health and effective regulatory action. The recent investigation by the European Parliament has severely criticised the approach the UK government and the Commission took (140). Not only was consumer safety compromised but the slowness in applying legislation has led to a period of crisis management with dramatic swings in consumer demand and heavy losses to the agricultural industry. Farmers have been compensated at a further cost to the UK and European taxpayer. The total costs of anti-BSE measures are now estimated to be between £300 million to £360 million a year. To date about £2.56 billion has been spent and it has been estimated that this could reach as high as £4.5 billion or more (141). In addition, there has been a considerable loss in consumer confidence both regarding the implementation of regulations and the trustworthiness of government and European institutions. For example, a recent survey, in the wake of the BSE crisis, reported that 75 per cent of respondents felt that it was very difficult to know if advice from the government about risks associated with food was independent of political pressures (142). Not surprisingly consumers are confused about who they can trust.

In spite of this, member state governments are still reluctant to take a precautionary approach to the potential public health risks that surround BSE where it may adversely affect producer interests. Concerned about the possible risk that sheep and goats had been exposed to BSE contaminated feed, in September 1996 Franz Fischler, the commissioner for agriculture, proposed prohibiting sheep brains, spleens and spinal cords from the human and animal food chains as a precautionary measure. France and the UK had already taken such steps unilaterally. The UK Meat and Livestock Commission argued that, 'although there is no evidence of BSE in sheep it is better to err on the side of caution' (143). However other member states have been unwilling to agree to such a measure, because of increased costs to their industries particularly in countries where they have had no outbreaks of BSE. The Spanish farm minister, for example, accused Fischler of 'sowing unjustified alarm through dangerous generalisations' (144). The Standing Veterinary Committee subsequently rejected a ban on a 12-2 vote, with Fischler forced to take his proposals to the Council of Ministers who similarly rejected them (145). A re-vote in July 1997 still did not achieve a qualified majority. Moreover, ten member states face formal infringement procedures for failing to implement EU legislation on the prevention and control of BSE (146).

The failure to adopt the precautionary principle in relation to BSE has already proved to have far-reaching and catastrophic effects both in terms of its threat to human health and also in its economic costs. We could apply the same argument to the current regulations concerning the use of antibiotics where their continued widespread use as growth promoters could have adverse implications for the maintenance of human health. Monitoring and enforcement of maximum residue levels (MRLs) is still not sufficient in many member states. Insufficient attention is being paid to the serious problem of the development of antibiotics resistance of bacteria including salmonella and e-coli and the very serious implications this has for human health. The Commission and Council of Ministers must take action to reduce the use of antibiotics in food production and this will require a move away from over-intensive farming methods.

Similarly, the injudicious and overzealous application of pesticides and fertilisers, encouraged by high support prices, may have unpredicted consequences for human health. Adoption of MRLs for pesticides has been particularly slow. It is only recently that a programme of re-evaluation of older pesticides has been established at EU level. Residues of pesticides above permitted levels are often found in fruit, vegetables, cereals, milk and drinking water and consumers are advised to peel their fruit and vegetables. High levels of nitrates have also been found in some vegetables, and water pollution is a serious and expensive problem. Again enforcement of the nitrate directive across the EU has been insufficient and variable. A reduction in the use of these chemicals is needed.

The development of biotechnology may provide healthier and less environmentally-damaging ways of producing food but, as with any new technology, it also carries risks. A precautionary approach to marketing approval is essential. The decision to approve the use of GM maize with an antibiotic resistant marker does not, in our view and that of the UK's Advisory Committee on Novel Foods and Processes, meet the precautionary principle. Poor regulatory decisions can take some time to have an impact and be extremely difficult and expensive to rectify, as BSE has shown. A mistake in the application of biotechnology – which raises concerns among consumers partly because of its novelty – could lead to rejection of all products of biotechnology regardless of their potential benefits.

Monitoring and enforcement

Regulations to protect consumer health and safety are not worth the paper they are written on if they are not enforced. Again the production-led approach to food production has led to insufficient attention being paid to monitoring and enforcement. Enforcement of regulations has been patchy across the EU and generally poor. The hormone ban has not been enforced effectively in many countries. Regulations to contain, eradicate, and protect consumers from BSE were not properly enforced for eight years. Systems for monitoring maximum residue levels for antibiotics, pesticides and nitrates are insufficient and enforcement mechanisms virtually non-existent. Enforcement of the nitrate directive is variable and inadequate. Monitoring and enforcement measures must be developed and improved. This will require improvements in traceability and more checking on farmers. There also needs to be much greater transparency about the results of monitoring exercises.

We have been campaigning for independent food agencies for both the UK and the EU since the late 1980s so that responsibility for regulation, inspection and enforcement could be clearly separated from the promotion of the food and agriculture industries' interests. It remains to be seen whether the arrangements being introduced in the Commission and those proposed for the UK (see appendix 2) will bring about the changes in culture and procedures needed to deliver an effective regulatory and enforcement system which really does put consumer health and safety first.

Producer responsibility

Policy-makers need to encourage producer responsibility for the potential harmful health and environmental impacts arising from the food production process all the way down the food chain. Currently primary agricultural products are excluded from the UK Consumer Protection Act and are not compulsory under the EU Product Liability Directive. The Commission's original 1976 proposal on product liability would have required all member states to include these products within the scope of their legislation, but this requirement was dropped and replaced by an option. Greece, Luxembourg, Sweden and Finland have taken up the option. The Commission now proposes to make the inclusion of these products in product liability legislation compulsory. We support this proposal.

Labelling

Another area of concern for consumer groups is the labelling of foodstuffs. Labelling is not a panacea and cannot be a substitute for regulation to ensure that products meet health and safety standards. But, consumers need to have accurate and meaningful information in order to choose what to buy. There is a directive on nutritional labelling, although this has not proved satisfactory and is being reviewed because consumers find the required format difficult to understand. There is now also a directive on quantitative ingredient listings which is to be adopted in 1998. However, given the concerns about certain agricultural practices, consumers should be given information about production processes to help them choose what they eat. Consumer groups have consistently argued that the products of GM technology should be labelled and welcome the Commission's intention to provide for this. Labelling is not only important for consumer confidence and choice, it is also important for competition. Producers who seek to gain any commercial benefits brought by the use of particular inputs or technologies should also bear the market risks. Unless food products are adequately labelled, farmers using a new method impose the commercial risks associated with it on to other farmers and the industry as a whole.

In addition to the information required by regulation a large number of industry quality assurance schemes have developed in recent years providing additional information for consumers. Not all consumers will want, or be able to afford, to pay the necessary premiums to obtain additional quality attributes but many do, so this is a welcome development. However, it also raises a number of consumer concerns.

Designing meaningful labelling schemes which provide genuine information to consumers is not straightforward. The information provided has to be verifiable, and independent arrangements in place to ensure that the information is verified, and that there are sanctions against those who attempt to mislead the consumer with false claims. This often depends on the existence of other monitoring schemes such as traceability schemes and treatment records for animals which need effective monitoring and enforcement arrangements in place. Sensitive detection tests may be required.

Labelling schemes require solid foundations otherwise they will do nothing to improve consumer confidence in the food industry or its regulators. There is also a danger of information overload if producers develop too many competing industry schemes, all with differing criteria. Our research on both environmental claims and health claims shows that this leads to consumer confusion and mistrust and does not help people make choices (147).

Recommendations

Scientific knowledge can never be complete and there are often areas of doubt or even conflicting opinion on matters of quality, safety and efficacy. Although the EU has a rigorous scientific testing programme in relation to chemical substances in agricultural production, ultimately 'safety' in relation to scientific assessment is about probabilities and not certainties. Decisions about the licensing and approval of new production processes, veterinary drugs, agri-chemicals and biotechnology are taken by governments on the basis of the probabilities generated by scientists and a balancing of risks against benefits. Lessons should be learnt from the case of BSE and such political decisions should always err on the side of caution particularly where there is a potential threat to human health.

Animal feed

Recommendation 5: The Council of Ministers should extend the EU ban on the use of mammalian meat- and bone-meal in feed for cattle and sheep to all animal feed, and should thoroughly evaluate the production processes for animal feed using the precautionary principle. It should introduce a compulsory full ingredient labelling scheme for all animal feed.

Hormones

Recommendation 6: The Council of Ministers should keep the current ban on the use of hormones in meat, and the moratorium on the use of BST in milk production in the EU in place. The Commission should ensure that member states enforce the bans.

Antibiotics

Recommendation 7: The Council of Ministers should prohibit the use of antibiotics as growth promoters throughout the EU. The use of antibiotics should only be allowed when an infection is diagnosed, and then under veterinary direction.

Pesticides and nitrates

Recommendation 8: The European Commission should ensure that all member states quickly and strictly implement the programme for the systematic re-evaluation of old pesticides.

Recommendation 9: The European Commission should develop a system for ensuring that maximum residue levels (MRLs) in food and maximum acceptable concentrations (MACs) in drinking water are monitored and enforced throughout the EU.

Monitoring and enforcement

Recommendation 10: The European Commission should bring forward proposals for improved identification and registration of sheep and pigs along the lines of that adopted for cattle.

Recommendation 11: The European Commission should bring forward proposals for compulsory treatment records for farm animals to enforce the hormone ban, and tighter regulations on the use of antibiotics.

Recommendation 12: The European Commission should ensure that monitoring of agricultural produce takes place in each member state to ensure compliance with EU regulations. The Council of Ministers should ensure that sufficient resources are transferred to DG XXIV (Consumer Policy) to ensure that this is possible.

Recommendation 13: The European Commission should co-ordinate and make publicly available the findings of surveillance on residues of veterinary medicines, pesticides and nitrates in foodstuffs in each member state.

Producer responsibility

Recommendation 14: The Council of Ministers should amend the Product Liability Directive to make the inclusion of primary agricultural products in national legislation compulsory.

11. The international framework

The emphasis of this report has been on European Union (EU) and national policy governing agriculture and its impact on consumers in terms of the price, choice, safety and quality of food. But European policy operates within the context of the global market place and the international rules agreed by governments for trade in food products. There has been much discussion both within and outside the consumer movement about the impact of the current arrangements, involving the international standards organisations, notably Codex, and the Uruguay Round of trade agreements concluded in 1994 and administered by the World Trade Organisation (WTO). There is concern that the benefits in terms of price and choice that the reductions in EU agricultural protectionism will bring, could be at the expense of much needed improvements in standards and consumer information.

The Codex Alimentarius

The Codex Alimentarius Commission was established in 1962 following recommendations from a joint Food and Agriculture Organisation (FAO) and World Health Organisation (WHO) conference on food standards. Its main objectives are to:

- protect the health of consumers and ensure fair practices in food trade;

- promote the co-ordination of all food standards work by international governmental and non-governmental organisations;

- determine priorities and initiate and guide the preparation of draft food standards with the aid of appropriate organisations; and

● finalise these standards and publish them as a 'Codex Alimentarius' (food code); and amend these standards as necessary.

Most countries in the world are members. To accomplish its objectives the Codex Alimentarius Commission has established an extensive network of committees. Control is exercised by full Commission meetings, held every two years. An executive committee is responsible for making proposals to the Commission about the work programme and most of the technical work is done by subsidiary committees, some of which meet every year. There are two main groups of committees, those dealing with subjects and those dealing with individual commodities. Codex also depends on the expert technical committees of the FAO and the WHO to advise on food additives and pesticide residues. These are the joint FAO/WHO Expert Committee on Food Additives (JECFA) and the Joint Expert Meeting on Pesticide Residues (JMPR).

Subject committees have responsibility for developing standards and codes on issues such as labelling, additives, contaminants, and sampling. These can then be applied to all food and are called 'horizontal standards'. The commodity committees, on the other hand, develop standards for individual items of food covering details like the composition, additives, contaminants and labelling for the specific food. These are called 'vertical standards'. About 200 commodity standards are agreed at present.

Development of any Codex standard usually follows a lengthy eight-step progression that allows for extensive consultation and discussion to arrive at a consensus. All member countries are allowed to attend meetings and if unable to attend, can submit written comments which are considered during the meetings. Consumer interest in the establishment of international food standards has now also been recognised and Consumers International has observer status at general (non-expert) Codex meetings. It is one of 111 observer organisations, over 100 of which are industry-funded groups. No observers are allowed at the meetings of the executive committee, or JECFA and JMPR.

It is seen as up to individual governments to establish links with consumers in their own countries, to ensure that the views expressed in the Commission take their interests into account. In 1992 the UK set up a National Codex Consultative Committee to discuss issues on specific subject areas before the international Codex meetings. Interested parties, including consumer organisations, have been invited to sit on this committee and to represent their views to government. Member countries can also invite observers to be part of their national delegations. When this happens the public interest representatives are vastly outnumbered by industry representatives. For example, at the Commission meeting in June 1995, the USA delegation included 27 delegates. Fourteen were government officials, 12 trade or industry representatives, and one represented a public interest group (148).

The Codex Alimentarius Commission is a voluntary organisation and once a Codex standard is published it is up to member countries to consider how to adopt it into national legislation. There is no compulsion to adopt a standard and overall they have not met with overwhelming success. The vast majority have only been taken up by a small proportion of countries. The EU, for example, sets its own standards which may be higher or lower than Codex standards.

However, following the WTO's 1994 Uruguay Round negotiations, the Codex Alimentarius Commission has been assigned a significant role not only in resolving trade disputes over food safety brought to arbitration through the WTO, but also, in providing the reference basis for the establishment of international standards.

The WTO agreements

The Uruguay Round Agreement established a permanent world trade body covering goods, services and intellectual property rights with a common disputes settlement procedure. The creation of the WTO aims to increase the status of international trading rules and ensure more effective advocacy and policing of the trading system. The following sections outline some of the new agreements reached as part of the package which are of interest to consumers and relevant to food and agriculture.

The Agreement on Agriculture

The 1994 Uruguay Round agreement on agriculture focuses on reducing trade distorting domestic support, import barriers and export subsidies.

Table 4 Main targets of the 1994 Uruguay Round

	Developed countries	Developing countries	Least developed countries
Domestic support	20% reduction over 6 years	13.3% reduction over 6 years	No reduction
Market access tariffs	Tariffs to be reduced by 36% over 6 years	Tariffs to be reduced by 24% over 10 years	No reduction
Export subsidies	36% reduction in value 21% reduction in quantity over 6 years	12% reduction in value 7% reduction in quantity over 10 years	No reduction

The reduction in domestic support does not apply to direct payments, for example environmental, regional and structural assistance, nor to production-limiting programmes such as the EU compensatory payments.

Non-tariff measures, for example quotas, variable import levies, and voluntary export restraints must be converted to tariffs (tariffication) and subject to the same reduction timescale. Existing import opportunities must be maintained and minimum access tariff quotas established where imports do not exceed 3 per cent of domestic consumption.

Additionally, 'peace' provisions largely prevent countries from protecting their markets against the repercussions of other nations' domestic support and export policies which comply with the agreement.

The extent to which the agreement negotiated and covered reductions in domestic support, import barriers and export subsidies was limited by the EU position which prevented the reforms from going beyond the 1992 CAP reform. This was a disappointment to EU consumers who will continue to face relatively high domestic prices, and the burden on the EU taxpayers will not be significantly lowered.

Food standards

The 1994 Uruguay Round agreement addressed product standards in two agreements: the agreement of sanitary and phytosanitary measures (SPS) and the technical barriers to trade (TBT) agreement. These aim to establish clearer rules on technical regulations, standards, and conformity assessment procedures to ensure that they do not create unnecessary barriers to international trade and to reduce the volume and importance of related trade disputes.

The SPS includes all measures taken by authorities to protect human, animal and plant health from the risks linked to the spread of pests and diseases, and from additives, contaminants or toxins in food. It is the main code for health and safety standards.

The main provisions of the agreement are:

- no discrimination between imported and domestically produced goods – food safety and animal and plant health protection measures must not be used to artificially protect markets from imports;

- explicit permission for countries to maintain or introduce measures which bring standards to higher levels than relevant international standards, provided that they are evaluated against scientific evidence and risk assessment;

- existing international standards, guidelines and recommendations, in particular those of the Codex Alimentarius, the International Office of Epizootics and the International Plant Protection Convention, will be encouraged to form the basis and reference for the establishment of national standards.

In addition, special provisions have been made in the agreement to encourage transparency.

The TBT agreement covers both the processing and production methods, and the final characteristics of all non-food products as well as regulations on aspects of food, for example, packaging and labelling, which are not directly relevant to health and safety. With a similar goal to the SPS, the TBT aims to ensure that trade restrictions on technical regulations are legitimate (they seek to protect human, animal and plant health or the environment) and that national rules do not constitute unnecessary barriers to trade. The requirement to use relevant international standards as a basis for national standards also applies, but the agreement recognises that variations between countries (climatic/geographic or fundamental technological implications) can justify different standards.

As a result, any country which sets and maintains standards higher than those accepted internationally and which do not comply with the terms of the agreements will have to amend their standards, pay compensation to potentially exporting countries or to make an equivalent arrangement, if they are successfully challenged in the WTO.

The consumer perspective

We support the development of internationally recognised standards for food and other products in order to protect consumers and facilitate trade. Equally we oppose the covert use of national standards as protectionist barriers to trade and competition. We also support the reduction in agricultural protectionism that will result from the Uruguay Round agriculture agreement. We look forward to further reforms from the next round of negotiations on agriculture due to start in 1999. However, support for freer trade does not mean that consumers should have to accept lower standards of consumer protection or be deprived of information they need to make informed choices.

The SPS agreement explicitly includes a provision that allows countries to introduce or maintain health and safety measures which are higher than the relevant international standards, if they can be justified on the basis of scientific evidence or risk assessment procedures. It also contains a provision which allows countries to introduce health and safety measures in cases where there is insufficient scientific evidence – a recognition of the precautionary principle. However, such action is seen as temporary. Countries are required to try and find the information needed for a 'more objective assessment of risk' within a reasonable period of time.

There are still many gaps in scientific knowledge and evidence, and certainty is not always achieved. In addition, as the results of different expert food safety committees illustrate, the conclusions and opinions surrounding the evaluation of certain products often differ and can be contradictory. Thus the interpretation is more a matter of opinion than of 'objective science'. Science is continuously revised in the light of further evidence and new risks. In some areas, scientific consensus does not exist as a basis for settling related trade disputes and it is important to apply the precautionary principle when in doubt. There is a danger that many judgements and decisions taken under the agreement will, in practice, rely on unjustifiably precise interpretation of incomplete scientific data. This, some would argue, is exactly what has happened in the EU/US hormones dispute.

The EU/US hormones dispute is the first test case under the SPS agreement and it is still working its way through the system. This is an unfortunate test case for consumers. The majority of EU consumer organisations strongly supported the introduction of the ban on hormones on health and safety grounds. There had been a number of food scares including the contamination of baby foods with residues of an illegal hormone, DES, which had heightened consumer concern. All the safety endorsements provided by scientific advisory committees were dependent on correct use. It was known that hormones were being incorrectly applied and that the abuse was difficult to trace.

However, while consumers' safety concerns were a factor in the EU's decision, managing the excesses of the CAP was also an important factor. The Agriculture Commissioner at the time, Frans Andriessen, made it clear publicly that it was a political decision, motivated by concern about the EU beef surplus on the theory that the hormone ban would reduce both domestic beef production and beef imports and thereby reduce the size of the beef mountain. At the time the ban was introduced there was wide consensus in the scientific community, both inside and outside the EU, that 'natural' hormones were safe provided they were properly used. However, experts have raised concerns about the carcinogenic effects of hormones and some take the view that any increase above levels occurring naturally imposes an additional risk which should not be accepted. The potential risks associated with cocktails of hormones (synergistic effects) about which little is known are also a cause for concern.

The WTO dispute panel found against the EU. The Bureau Européen des Unions de Consommateurs (BEUC) has been very critical of the panel's report on the grounds that it failed to take sufficient account of new scientific evidence presented to it (149). The EU appealed and the Appellate Body reported in January 1998. It found that the EU had not based its ban on a proper risk assessment in accordance with WTO rules but rejected or modified some of the panel's other arguments. If the appellate body's finding is upheld by the dispute settlement body the EU has three options:

- it can remove the hormone ban;

- it can keep it and offer compensation to those who have lost out as a result of the ban; or

- it can conduct a formal risk assessment and then adopt EU legislation on the basis of the new risk assessment.

The EU has announced its intention to pursue the third option. This will have to be completed in 15 months. In the meantime the EU can maintain the hormone ban (150).

As yet there have been no relevant challenges under the TBT agreement. The EU proposal to require the labelling of all GM food, a measure which consumers support, may well provide such a case. The TBT does not list the provision of information to consumers as a 'legitimate objective' for regulation. Information is a prerequisite for consumer choice, and choice is the mechanism by which consumers exert influence in markets and play their part in the competitive process which drives economic efficiency. The rationale for liberal trade policies is their positive impact on competition bringing economic efficiency and growth. Clearly labelling schemes can be designed in a way which unfairly discriminate against imports. They are a legitimate area of concern for the WTO which will wish to ensure that they meet its fundamental principles of national treatment and non-discrimination. But, if the TBT can really be interpreted in a way which limits consumer information schemes which are fairly applied, and thus limits consumer choice, it would be perverse.

While it is probably too early to be sure how these agreements will work in practice it is possible that they could be having a discouraging effect. Governments are certainly citing them as a reason (or excuse) for not introducing improvements in standards and information consumer groups would like to see.

If consumer organisations' worst fears prove to be justified there will be calls for revisions to the agreements which, if ignored, will lead to protectionist pressures. Both agreements are due for review by their respective WTO committees. It is essential that these reviews take on board consumer concerns and consider whether the agreements are likely to operate in a way which militates against improvements in standards and consumer information. If this is likely to be the case they must be amended.

The way the international standards setting organisations operate is also crucial. Consumer organisations have been very critical of the Codex, for example. The SPS agreement gives increased influence to Codex without addressing its weaknesses. Significant reform of its structure and decision-making to ensure that the consumer interest is better represented is essential if consumers are to have any confidence in its decisions.

One area of concern for consumers relates to the selection of experts who advise the Codex Commission on safety matters through joint FAO/WHO expert committees and who are selected by the parent bodies. According to the National Food Alliance examination of the composition of these expert committees in the 19th Session (1991) the industrialised countries of the north were heavily represented – 60 per cent while accounting for 14.6 per cent of the world's population – to the detriment of developing countries. The US sent 243 participants while overall, those representing African national delegations amounted to 142. Furthermore, industry and corporate interests outnumbered the public interest groups and governments of many countries. Out of the 2,578 participants, 660 represented industry interests and 26 public interest groups. 140 corporations were represented but only 105 nations (151). The application of health standards, set by international panels which are heavily influenced by industrial interests undermines democratic control and consultation procedures over food policy at national and regional level. It brings the ability and commitment of Codex to protect the public interest seriously into question.

To ensure that the expertise on toxicology and technology comes from a varied background and is not just confined to experts concentrated in, or funded by, food and chemical industries, the FAO/WHO should agree in consultation with consumer organisations a list of published criteria for selecting the experts for groups and committees. Consumer groups should take part in the selection process, and be able to nominate a number of experts.

Consumer participation is crucial in the procedures to set standards. However, to ensure the development of consumers' participation at international level it is essential that some further resources be allocated to consumer groups to strengthen their technical capacity and to increase the scope of their representation. At the 1997 Codex meeting only Norway included, and funded, a consumer representative on its delegation (152). In addition, a comprehensive policy on freedom of information within the Codex must be adopted to ensure the accessibility of technical and toxicological data. The principles of excellence, independence and accountability should apply to the Codex as they do to the EU's new structure of food standards committees.

Recommendations

Recommendation 15: The reviews of the World Trade Organisation Sanitary and Phytosanitary Standards agreement and Technical Barriers to Trade agreement must include an examination of whether they are likely to operate in a way which discourages improvements in standards and consumer information. If this is found to be the case the agreements must be amended.

Recommendation 16: The international community must agree to reform the Codex by:

- adopting a full freedom of information policy;

- committing additional resources to provide for better representation of consumer and developing country interests;

- opening up the expert committees to consumer participation; and

- reducing the dominance of food producers by: limiting the numbers that can attend meetings as observers or as part of national delegations; ensuring that experts are drawn from a wide variety of backgrounds; and requiring all experts who receive funding from industry to declare the details in a public register.

Appendix 1

Regulation of veterinary medicinal products

Licensing

No veterinary medicine can be marketed unless it has a licence. In keeping with procedures for human medicines, animal medicines are judged using the criteria of quality, safety and efficacy and licensed under regulations first drawn up under the 1968 Medicines Act. A company seeking a product licence must submit an application to the Veterinary Medicines Directorate (VMD) and pay a fee. The Veterinary Products Committee (VPC) advises the agriculture and health ministers, who are the licensing authority in the UK. Applications for variations to existing licences can be dealt with by the VMD working to VPC standards. A licence, once granted, is valid for 5 years although it can be revoked in an emergency. Once licensed medicines are put into one of four categories:

- the general sales list (GSL) which may be sold without restriction;

- the pharmacy and merchants list (PML) which may be sold by pharmacists, vets, and by merchants who have been trained and are registered with the Royal Pharmaceutical Society of Great Britain (RPSGB) or the Department of Agriculture Northern Ireland (DANI);

- the pharmacy list (P) which may be sold only by pharmacists and vets; and

- the prescription only medicines (POM) which are sold by vets or pharmacists on written prescription by vets.

A review of product licences for veterinary medicine granted before 1 January 1984 is being carried out by the VMD to ensure that products licensed in the UK meet the requirements laid down by EU directive 81/851/EEC. Manufacturers of animal medicines must also be licensed under the Medicines Act and regularly inspected by the Department of Health.

The Committee for Veterinary Medicinal Products (CVMP) was set up by the European Commission in 1983 under Directive 81/851/EEC. A member state must inform the Committee of any authorisations of veterinary medicinal products which they approve or of any withdrawals from the market. This is now working under the newly created European Medicines Evaluation Agency.

The EU has attempted to harmonise the system for licensing human and animal medicines so that a single licensing decision would enable a manufacturer to market a product through the EU. Companies may now apply for a product licence directly to the CVMP. In addition, there is a mutual recognition procedure. A company which has been given authorisation for a product in one member state can apply to two or more other member states with authorisation normally given within 120 days. However, a member state can lodge an objection with the CVMP within that time. The Mutual Recognition Facilitation Group of the CVMP then rules on whether the product meets the EU authorisation criteria. The Committee can also be asked to give an opinion where there is concern because a product is used in human therapy. In the past, under previous mutual recognition procedures, objections from member states have been the rule rather than the exception with member states unwilling to accept licences awarded by others.

Antibiotics

Like other veterinary medicines, the antibiotics used in feed have to be approved by the VPC. This use however, is regulated by the EU under a series of directives. Directive 70/524/EEC amended by 84/587/EEC sets out the conditions for licensing feed additives and Directive 90/167/EEC lays down conditions for the preparation, placing on the market, and use of medicated feedingstuffs in the EU. The EU Committee of Experts on Feed Additives, to which each member state sends delegates, and the Standing Committee for Animal Nutrition (SCAN) decide which additives will be permitted. The Annexes to the directive then list the antibiotics which can be incorporated into feedstuffs. Since July 1989 all UK incorporators of medicated animal feedstuffs have had to be registered with the RPSGB or DANI.

Residues

Applications for product licence must include information to satisfy the VMD that using the product will not leave harmful residues in food. Toxicological tests provide the so called 'No Observable Effect Level'. This is the level at which no effect in the most sensitive species is found. Since this is defined by animal experiments alone, directly extrapolating it to people would take no account of the unknown physiological differences in the responses of people and the species of laboratory animal. As a result, this level is then multiplied by a safety factor (usually a 100 times) to set the acceptable daily intake (ADI) in humans. The ADI is the maximum amount of a specified residue that an average person could eat every day in a lifetime without suffering harm. This is then divided up between foods in a normal diet to arrive at a maximum residue level (MRL) in the foodstuff that, even in dietary extremes, would not exceed the ADI for the particular substance concerned.

It is the CVMP and its working party on the safety of residues which advise on the MRLs to be set for each veterinary product. Definitive MRLs are placed in Annex I of Regulation 2377/90 and are legally binding. Some substances are not subject to an MRL and are put in Annex II. Annex III is the list of provisional MRLs pending additional data from the applicant for a product licence. Annex IV contains a list of banned substances.

In the UK, MRLs are recommended by the VPC and written into the veterinary medicine product licence. A withdrawal period (for use when a food producing animal is treated) is specified for each product to prevent residues appearing in the final food product.

In both the UK and EU there is a voluntary scheme for reporting suspected adverse reactions (SARs) to veterinary medicines whether the sufferer is animal or human. The holder of a product licence must keep a register of any SARs reported to it and make it available to VMD. If necessary the product is placed under surveillance and the batch may be withdrawn, product literature may be amended, or a product licence may be suspended or revoked. Not all EU member states have a scheme for collecting information on SARs. In order to coordinate information and to encourage and support member states to put their own systems in place, the EU operates its own SARs system, known as pharmacovigilance. This is overseen by the veterinary pharmacovigilance working party of the CVMP and operates on similar principles to that operating in the UK.

Residue surveillance

Under Directive 86/469/EEC, each member state must submit a forward testing plan for each year to look for hormones, antibiotics, nitrofurans, organochlorine and organophosphorus compounds, beta-agonists, heavy metals and a number of other medicinal products. The number of samples which must be taken is worked out statistically in terms of the numbers expected to be sent for slaughter and the breakdown of species within that number. In the UK surveillance is carried out by the National Surveillance Scheme (NSS).

Samples are collected on farms and at slaughterhouses at random from live animals and carcasses. Samples showing up residues above MRLs are traced back to the farm of origin or importer. Records are checked and suppliers traced if overdosing has resulted from feedstuffs. The results of sampling are published quarterly in MAVIS (Medicines Act Veterinary Information Service Bulletin) and in the Annual report of the VMD. Bulletins on fertiliser and pesticide residues are also regularly released by the MAFF Food Safety Directorate in their Food Surveillance Information Sheets.

In addition, concerned with the problems of zoonoses, that is, diseases that may be passed from animals to humans, Directive 92/117/EEC was introduced in 1992. This provides for the harmonisation of rules governing prevention of specific diseases. Member states are required to collect information on outbreaks of particular zoonoses (salmonellosis, brucellosis, tuberculosis and trichinosis) in humans and animals and to provide an annual report to the Commission on trends and sources of zoonotic infections recorded during the previous year. The Directive also requires member states to establish measures for the testing of breeding flocks of domestic fowl numbering 250 or more birds. Owners must arrange for their flocks to be tested every four weeks with samples being taken every 8 weeks under official supervision. Where the presence of Salmonella enteritidis or Salmonella typhimurium is suspected the Directive requires an investigation of the flock and compulsory slaughter if infection is confirmed.

Under COM (93) 441 the Commission has proposed legislation which will permit member states to impose strict and immediate financial or administrative penalties on producers found using banned substances.

Appendix 2

Institutional reform

United Kingdom

On 14 January 1998 the UK Government published a white paper setting out its proposals for a Food Standards Agency whose essential aim will be the protection of public health in relation to food. The agency will be a public body comprising a commission of no more than twelve independent members, a majority of which will be drawn from a public interest background. Its guiding principles will require it to work in an open, transparent and consultative way and to ensure that consumers have the information they need to make informed choices.

Food safety

The agency will advise ministers on all aspects of food hygiene policy and policy on the microbiological safety of food. It will be responsible for licensing fresh meat plants, and for measures to prevent the transmission of the BSE agent through the human food chain. It will take over responsibility for the Meat Hygiene Service and the dairy hygiene enforcement work carried out by the agriculture departments in England and Wales.

The agency will be responsible for policy on food additives and chemical contaminants in food, compositional standards of foodstuffs, and the labelling of food.

Novel foods

The agency will assess novel food applications and develop and implement policy on the control of novel food and processes. It will take over the agriculture ministers' responsibilities for issuing consents for the release of genetically modified organisms intended for food and animal feed, and will be responsible for licensing and inspecting food irradiation facilities.

Food safety on the farm

However, the agency will share responsibility with the agriculture departments for farm food safety issues. It will have safeguard powers to take action to prevent contaminated food from entering the food chain. It will be able to recommend that health ministers introduce additional statutory controls to those that agriculture departments have put in place if it considers this necessary in the interest of public health. It will share responsibility with agriculture departments for policy on animal feed, and play a role in developing and implementing policy to control animal diseases which may be passed through the food chain. Lead responsibility for the Pesticides Safety Directorate and the Veterinary Medicines Directorate will remain with MAFF.

Nutrition

The agency will be responsible for providing advice about the nutrient content of food and the diet as a whole. It will work with health departments in defining the health education message on nutrition issues and in developing policy advice to ministers. Health departments will remain responsible for health issues where nutrition is one of a number of risk factors.

Enforcement

The agency will work with local authorities (who will remain responsible for day-to-day food law enforcement) to encourage consistency in enforcement practice.

It will support the work of health authorities and local authorities in the investigation of food-borne illness, becoming directly involved where an incident extends beyond the local level, or where local investigation of an outbreak is not effective.

European Union

The organisation of food policy within the EU has been largely dispersed across a number of Directorates General (DG) of the European Commission, which are responsible for drafting legislation. These are DG III (Industry), DG VI (Agriculture) and DG XXIV (Consumer Policy). These DGs view food policy from different angles. DG III is concerned with market issues such as labelling, hygiene and standards as well as eliminating barriers to trade for processed food, while DG VI focuses on production issues such as agricultural produce, food quality, hygiene and standards.

Following the criticisms of the Commission over the handling of the BSE crisis the European parliament set up a temporary committee of enquiry on BSE in July 1996. The results, which were published in a report in February 1997, highlighted the problems linked to the absence of an integrated approach to public health. It recommended that transparency of the scientific committees should be promoted and their role shifted to a purely advisory one. It also suggested the creation of a Public Health Protection Unit 'responsible for the exercise and co-ordination of powers aimed at ensuring effective action on matters of food law, food quality and hygiene, human and animal health protection and consumer protection'. This could either be a separate DG or within a different DG, independent of agricultural and industrial interests.

In February 1997, Santer, the commission president, announced a series of reforms to tackle the priority of food safety and public health. These reforms are informed by the principle that responsibility for legislation should be separate from the responsibility for scientific consultation as well as from that for inspection. Greater transparency, information accessibility and dissemination are intended throughout the decision-making process and inspection measures. DG XXIV is being reorganised to be in charge of consumer health with the relevant scientific committees falling under its authority.

- There will be a change in the structure and scope of DG XXIV, which is now named Consumer Policy and Health Protection Directorate and has further resources and additional staff, with posts transferred from DG III and DG VI.

- The DG will establish a group of commissioners working on issues of food health, chaired by president Santer, to guide the follow-up to the recommendations of the temporary committee of enquiry's report.

- An interservice group chaired by the new Director General of DG XXIV will be created to ensure the co-ordination of consumer health issues across the different departments of the Commission.

- Scientific committees will now report to DG XXIV with the creation of a steering committee for the overall examination of their working procedures and for cross-sectoral review of issues which fall under the responsibility of different committees. This committee replaces the former multi-disciplinary scientific committee.

- A newly created unit for the assessment of public health risks and the inspection of foodstuffs will report directly to the Director General of DG XXIV.

- The Veterinary and Phytosanitary Services (DG VI) will be extended to what has been renamed the Product Quality Control and Audit Office, with its transferral to DG XXIV, aiming to monitor acceptable food hygiene, veterinary and plant health standards. This reorganisation and extension of the control service seeks to be independent, transparent in disseminating the results of inspection and control programmes, and will work closely with units drafting legislation, with scientific committees and with consumer and socio-economic interest groups.

- The rapid alarm system for dangerous products will be transferred from DG XXIV to DG III.

- Article 129A of the Maastricht Treaty will be extended to emphasise the profile of human health protection within the EU.

- Proposition that the European Parliament, instead of its current advisory role, be given powers of co-decision in the protection of human health and in the definition and implementation of relevant policies and measures in this field.

- A scientific conference on meat- and bone-meal in Brussels in July 1997.

A green paper on general principles of EU food law has been presented by the Commission with new amendments concerning food safety and consumer protection regarding transparency, subsidiarity and mutual recognition.

References

1. National Consumer Council, *Consumers and the Common Agricultural Policy*, HMSO, 1988.

2. Organisation for Economic Co-operation and Development, *Agricultural Policies, Markets and Trade: Monitoring and outlook*, Paris, 1997.

3. See reference 2.

4. European Commission, *Farm Incomes in the European Community in the 1980s*, Brussels, 1993.

5. European Commission, *EC Agricultural Policy for the 21st Century*, European Economy no. 4, Brussels, 1994.

6. European Commission, *A European Initiative on Transmissible Spongiform Encephalopathies (TSE)*, (COM (96) 582 final), Brussels, 1996.

7. See reference 6.

8. MAFF, *Programme to Eradicate BSE in the United Kingdom*, 1996.

9. *The Lancet*, vol. 349, 1 March 1997.

10. Spongiform Encephalopathy Advisory Committee (SEAC), 16 April 1997.

11. European Commission Decision 90/134/EEC, subsequently prolonged by Decision 92/450/EEC.

12. European Commission Decision 94/381/EEC.

13. See reference 6.

14. Consumers in Europe Group, *Bovine Spongiform Encephalopathy (BSE): Briefing and Recommendations from Consumers in Europe Group*, 96/13, 1996.

15. See reference 6.

16. See reference 8.

17. See reference 6.

18. See reference 14.

19. *Agra-Europe*, 3 October 1997.

20. MAFF Press Release, 3 December 1997.

21. See reference 14.

22. *The Economist*, 6 April 1996.

23. European Commission Decision 96/239/EC.

24. European Commission, *Situation and Outlook: Beef Sector*, Brussels, 1997.

25. *Agra-Europe*, 24 October 1997.

26. See reference 25.

27. Economic and Social Committee of the European Communities, *Own Initiative Opinion on BSE Crisis and Its Wide-ranging Consequences for the EU*, ESC 888/96, Brussels, 1996.

28. *Financial Times*, 27 November 1996 and *Liberation*, 26 November 1996.

29. See reference 27.

30. *Agra-Europe*, 12 July 1996.

31. European Commission Decision 94/381/EEC.

32. See reference 6.

33. See reference 14.

34. See reference 6.

35. *Agra-Europe*, 14 June 1996.

36. See reference 35.

37. European Commission Decision 95/287/EEC.

38. *Agra-Europe*, 8 November 1996.

39. European Commission Decision 89/469/EEC.

40. Council Regulation EC820/97.

41. 'The World Trade Organisation cuts its teeth on a beefy trade dispute', *The Cargill Bulletin*, vol 4, no. 5, October 1996, pp. 1-6.

42. See reference 41.

43. 'Hormones et autres résidus dans la viande bovine', *Test-Achats*, no. 373, January 1995, pp. 4-9.

44. European Commission, *Scientific Conference on Growth Promotion in Meat Production 29 Nov-1 Dec 95*, Report and Conclusions, 1995.

45. See reference 43.

46. Consumers in Europe Group, *Meat and Medicine: Human health, safety and animal pharmaceuticals*, 1994.

47. See reference 44.

48. See reference 44.

49. Council Directive 81/602/EEC.

50. Council Directive 88/146/EEC.

51. Council Directive 86/469/EEC

52. European Commission memo 95/153.

53. See reference 46.

54. *Test-Achats*, 1994.

55. European Commission, *Scientific Conference on Growth Promotion in Meat Production*, Press Release IP/95/1270, 21 November 1996.

56. See reference 43.

57. See reference 44.

58. European Commission memo 95/153.

59. See reference 44.

60. See reference 43.

61. *Agra-Europe*, 2 August 1996.

62. Consumers in Europe Group, *Bovine Somatotropin: Comments by the Consumers in Europe Group on the proposal from the Commission to extend the moratorium on the licensing of BST*, 94/16, 1994.

63. See reference 44.

64. Council Decision 90/218/EEC, amended by 91/61/EEC and 93/718/EEC.

65. Council Decision 94/936/EC.

66. See reference 62.

67. Economic and Social Committee of the European Communities, *Own Initiative Opinion of the Economic and Social Committee of the European Communities on the Use of Bovine Somatotropin in the European Union*, Brussels 14-15 September 1994.

68. See reference 67.

69. See reference 62.

70. See reference 67.

71. *Agra-Europe*, 4 July 1997.

72. S. Lange and E. Ek, *On Putting the Argument for Banning or Tightly Controlling the Use of ABs as Feed Additives.* Paper given to the Proceedings of the World's Poultry Science Association, 10th European Symposium on Poultry Nutrition, Turkey, 15-19 October 1995, pp. 208-218.

73. See reference 72.

74. See reference 46.

75. Written European Parliament question to Jacques Santer from Martina Gredler, a German MEP, tabled July 1995.

76. *Which?*, March 1997.

77. G A Jacoby and G L Archer, 'New mechanisms of bacterial resistance antimicrobial agents, *New England Journal of Medicine*, no. 324, 1991, pp. 601-612.

78. Swedish Farmers' Association, 1996.

79. D. Siegel, W.G. Huber and F. Enloe, 'Continuous non-therapeutic use of antibacterial drugs in feed and drug resistance of the gram-negative florae of food-producing animals, *Antimicrobial Agents and Chemotherapy*, no. 6, 1974, pp. 697-701.

80. H.P. Endtz, G.J. Ruiks and Van Klingeren, 'Quinoline resistance in campylobacter isolated from man and poultry following the introduction of fluoroquinolones in veterinary medicine', *Journal of Antimicrobial Chemotherapy*, no. 27, 1991, pp. 199-208.

81. E.J. Threlfall, B. Rowe and L.R. Ward, 'A comparison of multiple drug resistance in salmonellas from humans and food animals in England and Wales, 1981-1990', *Epidemiological Infection*, no. 111, 1993, pp. 189-197.

82. See reference 81.

83. Swedish Farmers' Association, 1996.

84. See reference 80.

85. See reference 72.

86. Bureau Européen des Unions de Consommateurs (BEUC), *Antibiotics in Animal Production*, 82/96, 1996.

87. Swedish Farmers' Association, 1996.

88. *Agra-Europe*, 31 January 1997.

89. See reference 46.

90. See reference 46.

91. World Resources Institute, *Pesticides and the Immune System: The public health risks*, 1996.

92. See reference 91.

93. C.M. Benbrook with E. Groth III, J. Halloran, M.K. Hansen, S. Marquardt, *Pest Management at the Crossroads*, Consumers' Union, 1996.

94. See reference 93.

95. See reference 93.

96. 'L'agriculture biologique', *Test-Achats*, October 1995.

97. *Agra-Europe,* 17 May 1996.

98. MAFF Press Release, *Results of Survey of Pesticides Residues in Milk*, 2 April 1996.

99. Environment Agency, 1996.

100. The Pesticide Trust, *Pesticides in Water*, Briefing, 1994.

101. European Commission, *Service du Porte Parole*, 23 July 1996.

102. See reference 99.

103. See reference 93.

104. See reference 93.

105. Council Directive 97/41/EC.

106. 'Les nitrates dans l'alimentation', *Test Santé*, no. 10, November 1995.

107. See reference 106.

108. See reference 106.

109. MAFF Food Safety Directorate, *Nitrate in Vegetables*, Food Surveillance Information Sheet no. 91, July 1996.

110. B.S. Frederiksen, 'European Commission Nitrate Policy', *Journal of Environmental Planning and Management*, vol. 38, no. 2, 1995, pp. 253-263.

111. Council Directive 80/778/EEC.

112. European Environment Agency, *The Environment in the European Union*, Copenhagen, EUR-OP, 1995.

113. Council Directive 91/676/EEC.

114. See reference 110.

115. See reference 110.

116. European Commission, *Communication on European Water Policy*, (COM(96) 59 final), 21 February 1996.

117. Consumers' Association, *Gene cuisine – a consumer agenda for genetically modified foods*, 1997.

118. *Agra-Europe*, 22 March 1996.

119. *Frankfurter Allgemeine Zeitung,* 14 November 1996.

120. European Commission Opinion VI/7893/96.

121. Advisory Committee on Novel Foods and Processes, *The Use of Antibiotic Resistance Markers in Genetically Modified Plants for Human Food: clarification of principles for decision-making*, 1996.

122. *The Times*, 18 February 1997.

123. *Agra-Europe*, 12 September 1997.

124. Council Directive 90/220/EEC.

125. *Agra-Europe*, 31 July 1997.

126. *Financial Times*, 20 November 1997.

127. European Community of Consumer Co-operatives, *Decisive Years for European Consumer Protection: Information, reflections for discussion and opinions*, Brussels, 1995.

128. Bureau Européen des Unions de Consommateurs (BEUC), 1996.

129. Swedish Farmers' Association, 1996.

130. Consumers in Europe Group, *The Rural White Paper: Comments by the Consumers in Europe Group*, 95/07, 1995.

131. Swedish Farmers' Association, *Sweden's Farmers Towards Sustainability*, 1996.

132. Swedish Farmers' Association, *Sweden's Farmers on their Way to the World's Cleanest Agriculture*, 1996.

133. See reference 131.

134. J. Pretty, *Regenerating Agriculture*, Earthscan, London 1995.

135. See reference 130.

136. European Commission Regulation 2092/91.

137. European Commission Regulations 2328/91 and 2078/92.

138. P. Bailleux and A. Scharpe, *Organic Farming*, EUR-OP, Luxembourg, 1994.

139. F.M. Brouwer and S. van Berkum, *CAP and the Environment: Analysis of the effects of the CAP on the environment and an assessment of existing environmental conditions in policy*, Agricultural Economics Research Institute, The Hague, 1995.

140. *Libération*, 27 November 1996.

141. *Agra-Europe*, 29 August 1997.

142. Consumers' Association, *Consumer Policy Review*, May/June 1996.

143. *Agra-Europe*, 6 September 1996.

144. See reference 143.

145. *The Independent*, 20 December 1996.

146. Consumers in Europe Group, 1997.

147. National Consumer Council, *Green Claims*, 1995 and *Messages on Food,* 1997.

148. Consumers' Association, 'Codex Alimentarius in the Consumer Interest?', *Consumer Policy Review*, vol. 7, no. 7, July/August 1997.

149. Bureau Européen des Unions de Consommateurs (BEUC), *BEUC Comments on the Report of the (WTO) Panel on EC Measures Concerning Meat and Meat Products (Hormones)*, Brussels, September 1997.

150. European Commission, *Hormone Meat: WTO judgement on EU ban just one step in a long process – consumer protection will be upheld!*, Background Note from DG XXIV, January 1998.

151. Consumers in Europe Group, *Codex Alimentarius Commission – Brief by Consumers in the European Community Group*, 93/18, 1993.

152. See reference 148.

Other National Consumer Council publications

We publish a wide range of other policy papers, reports and handbooks on current consumer issues. These are just a few of our recent titles.
To find out more about NCC books, please phone us on **0171 730 3469**.

In the Bank's Bad Books How the banking code of practice works for customers in hardship, 1997, 104 pages, £14

Unclear Waters Consumer prices and water company financial information, 1997, 52 pages, £12

Unfair Trading Recommendations for reform of Part III of the Fair Trading Act, 1997, 37 pages, £6

Regulating the Public Utilities A response to the DTI review of utility regulation, 1997, 35 pages, £6

NHS Complaints Procedures: The First Year, 1997, 49 pages, £8

Consumers and the Environment: Can Consumers Save the Planet? 1997, 113 pages, £14

Consumer Concerns 1997 Consumers' views of shops and shopping, 1997, 58 pages, £10

A-Z of Ombudsmen A guide to Ombudsman schemes in Britain and Ireland, 1997, 320 pages, £14

Electricity Takeovers The Implications for consumers, 1997, 82 pages, £14

Government and Consumers A consultation document, 1997, 74 pages, £14

Green Claims A consumer investigation into marketing claims about the environment, 1996, 216 pages, £14.50

These prices include postage and packing.

To order any of these books, please write to:
NCC Publications, 20 Grosvenor Gardens, London SW1W ODH
Please send a cheque with your order, payable to: *National Consumer Council.*